A Rockhounding Guide

to North Carolina's Blue Ridge Mountains

BY MICHAEL STREETER

almond, nc

3rd printing July 2011

Milestone Press, Inc., P.O. Box 158, Almond, NC 28702
www.milestonepress.com

Book design by Ron Roman/Treehouse Communications
www.treehousecomm.com

Cover and interior photos by Michael Streeter

Specimens pictured on pp. 40 and 98 appear courtesy of the Bill Booth Collection in Cherokee, N. C. Specimens pictured on p. 52 appear courtesy of the George McCannon Collection in Canton, N. C.

Library of Congress Cataloging-in-Publication Data

Streeter, Michael, 1957-
A rockhounding guide to North Carolina's Blue Ridge Mountains / by Michael Streeter.
p.cm.
Includes bibliographical references and index.
ISBN 1-889596-15-9 (alk. paper)
1. rocks—Collection and preservation—North Carolina. 2. Rocks—Collection and preservation—Blue Ridge Mountains. 3. Minerals—Collection and preservation—North Carolina. 4. Minerals—Collection and preservation—Blue Ridge Mountains. 1. Title.

QE445.N8S87 2003
552.09756'8—dc21

2002044891

Dedication

This book is dedicated to my partner and wife, Chris.
There is no more beautiful gem.

Preface

The main purpose of this guide is to provide as much current information as possible on collecting fine rocks and minerals that abound in the western North Carolina mountains. This book is also intended to show the breathtaking beauty that often surrounds mines and prospects, and to offer a sense of the long and storied history of mining, which has helped fuel local economies for over two centuries.

It is refreshing to know that even in this high-tech era of fast food and multi-billion dollar amusement parks, immense satisfaction can be derived from something as simple as rock and mineral collecting. In most cases, all that is needed to recover beautiful gemstones are a few directions, proper tools, and a modicum of elbow grease. Whether you are young or old, it is exciting to uncover gems that have been hidden in rock and soil for millions of years. It can be an awesome, emotional experience to see an emerald, sapphire, or aquamarine crystal sparkling in the sunlight for the first time since it was formed over 70 million years ago. It's no less inspiring to witness mother nature's amazing ability to reclaim the land surrounding old mines, transforming long-abandoned shafts and open pits into dark, mysterious ponds and rocky tailing piles into lushly forested slopes bright with wildflowers.

At the risk of sounding politically incorrect, I believe that rock and mineral collecting somehow satisfies our male and female hunting and gathering instincts. When visiting a site with a mixed group of rockhounds, I often observe that the majority of girls and women spend the bulk of their days surface collecting to find gems (gathering) while the boys and men will dig deep holes or break rock to bag their prizes (hunting). This gender difference works wonderfully at certain sites where collecting requires both the digging and the sorting of materials. While testosterone-charged men dig holes and impatiently fling out dirt like badgers on steroids, their better halves carefully pick through the soils, recovering gems that would otherwise have gone unnoticed. The gathering process also allows mothers the time to nurture their young children. I have never seen a small child's eyes fail to light up when handed a crystal.

Most rockhounds, myself included, are merely over-aged children who have refused to entirely grow up. I could go on with more of my pseudo-anthropological meandering, but the hole I have dug for myself is probably deep enough.

Contents

INTRODUCTION 8

HOW TO USE THIS BOOK 12

ROCKHOUNDING TOOLS 14

CONDUCT IN THE FIELD 18

PERMISSION TO COLLECT 19

SAFETY 19

COLLECTING SITES BY COUNTY

Avery County
Cranberry Iron Mine 22

Buncombe County
Black Mountain Kyanite 26
Goldsmith Mine 28

Cherokee County
Hitchcock Mine 32
Murphy Limonite after Pyrite 34
Vengeance Creek 36

Clay County
Behr Corundum Mine 40
Buck Creek 42
Corundum Knob 44

Haywood County
Chambers Mountain Kyanite 48
Wood Creek 50
Old Pressley Sapphire Mine 52
Redmond Prospect 54

Jackson County
Ruby City 58
Sheepcliff Mine 60

Macon County 63

Madison County
Little Pine Garnet Mine 66
Shut-In Creek Unakite 68
Stackhouse Mines 70

McDowell County
Woodlawn Limestone Quarry 74

Mitchell County
Abernathy Mine 78
Bandana Dolomitic Marble 80
Sinkhole Mine 82
Chalk Mountain Mine 84
Crabtree Emerald Mine 86
Deer Park Mine 88
Hootowl Mine 90

Swain County
Nantahala Talc & Limestone Quarry 94

Transylvania County
Grimshawe Mine 98

Yancey County
Mas-Celo Kyanite Mine 102
Ray (Wray) Mine 104

Appendix
Glossary 108
Resources 111
References 118
Index of Minerals and Collecting Sites 120
Field Notes 122

Introduction

Land of Minerals

North Carolina has long been a magnet for rockhounds. Few states compare favorably when it comes to North Carolina's rich abundance of rocks and minerals. To date, 311 minerals with 39 different gem varieties have been identified, but undoubtedly more remain to be discovered (Wiener and Ballew 1995). Over 30 rocks and minerals have been commercially exploited, making mining one of North Carolina's most important industries.

A Naturally Beautiful Setting

The natural beauty of North Carolina's gems is matched only by the Blue Ridge Mountains' spectacular scenery, with each season adding its own special touch to the panorama. In the summer the mountain peaks and ridges rise above lush green valleys like bluish ghosts looming tall behind a smoky haze that envelopes the landscape. With the coming of autumn, the summer haze gives way to clear blue skies, and the countryside is awash with vibrant colors as the leaves change from green to red, orange, yellow, and brown. The leaves fall from the trees, allowing for dramatic unobstructed views, and then winter arrives. High mountain peaks become frosted with sparkling white rime and occasional blankets of snow. Springtime does a two-step with winter, coming and going before it finally decides to stay. The leaves return, and the gray landscape becomes green again with splashes of white, yellow, and varying shades of pink from countless flowering plants and trees.

A Rich Geologic and Mineralogical History

The Blue Ridge Mountains of western North Carolina are rich with collectible rocks and minerals that formed during a long and complex geologic history. Rock formations as old as 1,100 million years have been overlain and intruded by younger rocks. Some of these younger rock formations, including the Chilhowee Group, Shady Dolomite, and Murphy Marble, originated in a sea, known as the Ocoee Basin, that formed just to the east of the North American continent about 800 million years ago (Beyer 1991). Dogtooth calcite and quartz crystals can be found in the Shady Dolomite at the Woodlawn Quarry in McDowell County. Talc, marble, and other associated minerals are found in the Murphy Marble belt in Swain and Cherokee Counties.

Corundum bearing smaragdite found on Chunky Gal Mountain in Clay Co.

Thick layers of mud, sand, and volcanic ash deposited in the Iapetus Sea to the east of the Ocoee Basin as long ago as 840 million years ago were metamorphosed into rock that would become known as the Ashe Metamorphic Suite. The Ashe Metamorphic Suite was pushed westward as much as 125 miles on massive thrust faults during successive mountain-building events that began about 505 million years ago. During this 255 million-year period in which the North American tectonic plate collided with the Euro-African plate, superheated waters saturated with silica and other minerals escaped from magmas buried deep within the earth's surface through fractures in the crust. Slow cooling and/or high pressures allowed crystallization of unusually large and exotic minerals forming pegmatite dikes (Beyer 1991). Pegmatites in Swain, Macon, Jackson, Transylvania, Mitchell, Buncombe, Avery, and Yancey Counties are renowned sources of feldspar, muscovite, quartz, uranium minerals, kyanite, tourmaline, and gem-quality garnet, ruby, sapphire, aquamarine, emerald, and apatite. It is also believed that dunite and peridotite bodies were intruded sometime during this period as is evidenced by the corundum-bearing dunite and peridotite bodies in Clay, Macon, Yancey, Jackson, Buncombe, and Mitchell Counties.

The past 250 million years—tame compared to the earlier great mountain building events—is marked by continued regional uplift accompanied by extensive subaerial erosion and deposition. It has been estimated that some 9,000 ft. of Blue Ridge rock have been eroded away (Wiener and Merschat 1990). Some of this detritus makes up the Atlantic and Gulf Coastal Plain sedimentary accumulations, while other material remains to this day on the Blue Ridge Mountain's slopes, valleys, and creeks. The Cowee Valley rubies and sapphires in Macon County, the Vengeance Creek staurolite and Murphy limonite in Cherokee County and the Buck Creek garnet and corundum in Clay County all represent the depositional remains of eroded rocks.

Mining in Western North Carolina through the Centuries

At least 2,500 years before Christopher Columbus set foot on the shore of what was to become our United States, Native Americans were mining the Appalachian Mountains of western North Carolina. In accounts from 1875 and 1876, geologists reported finding evidence of old mica mining in Mitchell County. They noted numerous prospect pits dotting the hillsides, some of which were very extensive, with trees 3 ft. or more in diameter rooted on large spoil mounds next to the pits. It is thought that Native Americans worked these mines for mica, which they used for ornaments, and/or for kaolin, a weathering product of

Old mining equipment at the Hitchcock Mine near Murphy

Introduction (continued)

Grimshawe Mine in Transylvania County

feldspar. It has been reported that prior to 1744, the Cherokee Indians mined and sold partially kaolinized feldspar to Europeans, presumably for shipment to England for ceramic use (Watts 1913; Stuckey 1965).

Mica from North Carolina has been discovered in ceremonial mounds built by the ancient Adena and Hopewell Native Americans in the Ohio Valley. The Adena probably came to North America in 1000 BC and existed until about AD 100. The Hopewell culture dates from approximately 100 BC to about AD 400. These early Native Americans were most likely traders who traveled extensively throughout the area that would become the eastern, southeastern, and midwestern United States. Materials such as copper from the Great Lakes, mica from North and South Carolina, and shells from the Gulf of Mexico are found in uncovered mounds throughout the Ohio Valley. These early Native Americans probably acquired these materials by trading for flint, a very hard and common material found all over the Ohio region (Arrangements.com; Ohiokids.org).

In the early 1540s, Spanish explorer Hernando DeSoto led an expedition that meandered its way throughout the present-day southeastern and midwestern United States. The King of Spain had given "Governor DeSoto" four years to colonize and hold America from the Port of Havana, Cuba. Part of DeSoto's ambitious plan to entice Spanish settlers to his new American colony was to bring back reports of the riches he found along the way. In 1540, DeSoto led his expedition into western North Carolina through present-day Tryon. His unsuccessful search for gold and silver would lead him on a westerly track through present-day Hendersonville, Asheville, Waynesville, Sylva, and Bryson City. (Clayton and Knight, Jr. 1993).

During and immediately following colonization of America, the search for base and precious metals, including copper, iron, and lead, was the primary focus of mining in western North Carolina. An iron industry consisting of small iron furnaces scattered throughout the region prospered during the 18th and 19th centuries and became a major stabilizing factor for the newly formed United States. Clays, mica, barite, and various other stones and minerals were also important nonmetallic materials produced during this period (Broadhurst 1955).

During the first half of the 20th century, more easily available reserves of metallic materials were discovered and exploited in other states and countries, bringing the end of metallic mineral mining in North Carolina. This gave rise to the exploration and mining of other rocks and minerals, including mica, feldspar, beryl, kyanite, quartz, olivine, corundum, talc, and marble. Thousands of mica mines scattered throughout western North Carolina were worked into the early 1960s until cheaper overseas sources made them no longer economical. Barite, corundum, kyanite, talc, quartz, marble, olivine, and beryl mines eventually succumbed to the same fate (Stuckey 1965).

Mining for garnets in Little Pine Garnet Mine in Madison County

Today, western North Carolina continues to be a major producer of feldspar and high-quality quartz, primarily from the Spruce Pine District in Mitchell County. Crushed stone is also produced in great quantities at numerous quarries, including the Nantahala Limestone & Talc Quarry in Swain County.

Modern rock and gem collecting in western North Carolina began as an extension of the commercial mining of rocks and minerals. For instance, exotic gems such as aquamarine, emerald, sapphire, and garnet are commonly found where mica was mined from granite pegmatites. During commercial mining operations, a mica miner's only interest was to recover as much mica as he could. A miner was not interested in any other mineral besides what he was paid to recover, which would help feed his family. Ironically, many of the minerals discarded as nuisances by mica miners would decades later become far more valuable than the mica itself. The Ray (Wray) Mica Mine dumps in Yancey County are known to contain some of the finest aquamarine crystals in North Carolina. For more than 40 years, rockhounds have been digging in the spoil piles surrounding the old mines, searching for long-ago discarded gems. Similar stories hold true for all but a few of the collecting localities detailed in this book.

Visit www.mcrocks.com for the latest collecting site updates.

How To Use This Book

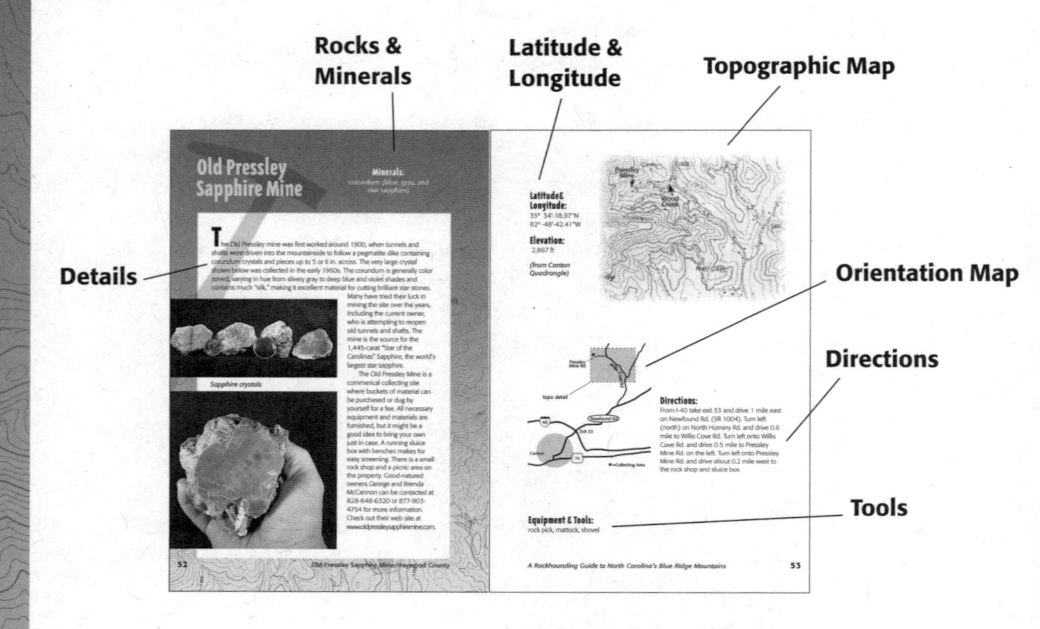

This guide is broken into three main parts. In the front you'll find general information to get you "up and running" for rockhounding in western North Carolina. The collecting sites, which constitute the bulk of the book, are located in the middle of it. They are listed in alphabetical order by county.

Above is a typical mineral-collecting area page spread. For each site, the name as well as the **Rocks & Minerals** to be found at each location are listed first. Also on the spread will be a black and white photograph of at least one of the most prominent rocks or minerals to be found there. (A color photograph of each rock and mineral, with a page number referencing it to the text, is included in the very last section of this book.) **Details** follows with the history of the site, when known.

Latitude & Longitude and **Elevation**, along with **Directions** to the site, give detailed information on location. Two maps are provided for each location. A **Topographic Map** provides detailed topographic characteristics of the immediate collecting area. A simple **Orientation Map** shows route numbers, nearby towns, and pertinent landmarks mentioned in the text. All maps in the book are oriented north and the scale of the topos is $^1/_2$ inch = approximately 1 mile. I've also included a list of recommended **Tools** to recover the best specimens at the site.

Several sections in the front of the book are worth a mention here. Those new to rockhounding will appreciate the **Tools** section. Knowing how to use a tool and what it looks like (if you need to go buy one) is imperative. **Conduct in the Field** outlines a code of ethics established by the American Federation of Mineral Societies. Since irresponsible collecting can damage the environment as well as the opportunities for future rock collecting at a given site, it is critical that collectors abide by these guidelines. Likewise, the section titled **Permission To Collect** provides essential information on gaining access to any site located on private property. A short section on **Safety** is a reminder that each collector assumes sole responsibility for him- or herself while collecting.

In the back, I've included a **Glossary** to explain some of the many scientific and rock-collecting terms which appear here. **References**, listed alpha-betically by author, are also provided at the back of the book. In the text, sources are indicated in parentheses.

A Note about Maps, Mapping Programs, and GPS

Maps are imperative for finding collecting sites. Each map in this book was taken from the U. S. Geological Survey (USGS) map indicated in the caption. It is very important to obtain a full USGS 7.5-minute (quadrangle) map of each site before heading out into the field. USGS maps can be purchased at many sporting goods stores, cartography shops, U. S. Forest Service offices, or directly from the USGS. To get a copy of their catalog, write to the Geological Survey at Box 25286, Federal Center, Denver, CO 80225, or call 303-236-7277. You may also visit the USGS website to find out how to order maps at http://mac.usgs.gov/mac/findmaps.html.

A source for free online topographic maps is Topozone.com. The interactive maps at this website can be quite useful for pinpointing locations and getting a feel for the general area.

The "Cadillac" of computer topographic map programs is Terrain Navigator 2001, developed by Maptech in Amesbury, Massachusetts. Terrain Navigator 2001 combines regional collections of digitized topographic maps with powerful PC navigation software for 2-D and 3-D viewing, customizing, printing and Global Positioning System (GPS) use. You can easily input the latitude and longitude provided for each site into the Terrain Navigator 2001 program, and it will take you right to the spot. Call Maptech at 888-839-5551 or visit their web site at www.maptech.com.

A GPS handheld receiver is a useful tool for finding a site by using the latitude and longitude. Remember that electronic units can fail. It is advisable to always carry a map and compass into the field to back up your GPS receiver.

Rockhounding Tools

Showing up at a collecting site with fancy tools may get you approving nods from fellow rockhounds, but you need to know how to best use your arsenal if you want to bring home the really good stuff. Although every collecting site is unique, many geologic environments are similar enough to each other that they require the same basic tools and techniques.

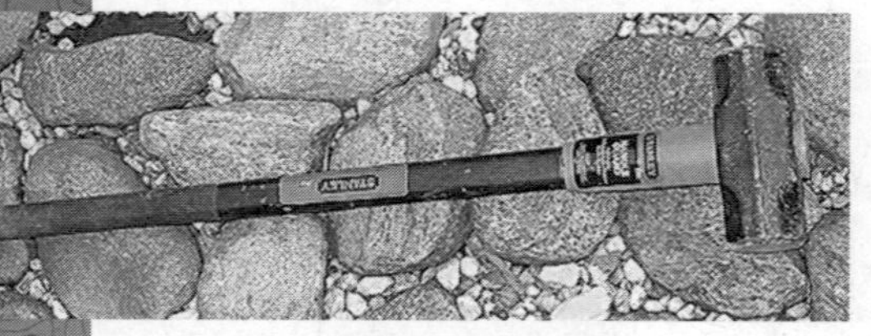

12-pound sledgehammer

"Heavy Artillery" Tools

Some rock-collecting sites, such as in the Redmond Prospect adit in Haywood County, consist mostly of solid rock. This hard-rock mining is physically challenging, but can be made easier with experience and the right tools. Hard-rock geologic settings require the "heavy artillery" tools, including sledge and crack hammers, chisels, gad points, and prybars. The only way to get to and liberate the gems and minerals is to break the rock. A sharp, flat-ended chisel struck with a crack hammer or small sledgehammer will pry apart and widen natural fractures or cracks in a rock. A gad point or pointed chisel can be used in the same fashion when a natural fracture is not wide enough to accommodate a flat-ended chisel, or to create a crack in solid rock. It is important to use only chisels that are sharp; trying to break rock with a dull chisel is like trying to cut a tough steak with a butter knife. Some collectors, including myself, prefer to use chisels with hand guards (see photo below) whenever possible to minimize the chance of whacking our chisel hands. Always wear gloves and safety glasses when breaking rock, as your collecting day will come to an abrupt and painful halt if you get hit in the eye with a rock fragment or metal shard.

Once a large crack has been established in a rock, it may be possible to insert a prybar into the crack to completely break the rock apart. The size of the prybar depends on the size and strength of the rock you are trying to split or move. A screwdriver can be used to pry away

Assorted chisels

Crack hammer and 6-pound sledge

small pieces of rock to safely recover delicate gems in pockets. In some places, the rock is so hard and fracture-free that the use of hammer and chisel is futile. In these instances, using a large (12- to 20-pound) sledgehammer may be the only way to break the rock. Be sure to have all your buddies duck behind trees while you are whacking away, as rock fragments will likely be flying around in all directions like errant bullets. Having a rock fragment bounce off your friend's forehead is never as funny as you imagined it would be.

Digging Tools

Gems and minerals are often found buried in soils. In this case, a pointed shovel will generally be your most important tool. A pick can be useful when the soils are hard or there are gravels and loose rocks to dig through. A small hand-held saw or weedcutter is nice to have on hand to cut roots that invariably get in the way of digging. Some sites, such as at the Wood Creek Sapphire Mine in Haywood County, require digging down to a gravel layer where gems may be found. Once you reach the gravel,

Large digger-prybar and rock hammer

Rockhounding Tools (continued)

Geopick or hoepick or mattock

Safety glasses and leather gloves

gems can be isolated by sifting and sorting the soils using a rock sifter or screen like the one pictured on p. 17. Dip the sifter repeatedly up and down, rocking it back and forth in water. This action causes the finer-grained soils to wash away, leaving behind washed gravel that may contain gems.

Abandoned mine tailings are often composed of assorted sizes of rocks and boulders that may be piled up or buried beneath soils or other forest debris. The Ray Mine in Yancey County is a prime example of this type of environment, where large rocks and boulders dumped by mining operations cover large areas of steep mountain slopes. The gems and minerals may be found loose or still attached to the rocks and boulders. Many minerals can be found simply by walking back and forth over the tailings and by turning over rocks. If you want to dig at this type of location, it often works well to use a pick and shovel to dig horizontally into the slope of the tailings. Digging horizontally into a slope establishes a "wall" that allows a rock collector to more easily pick out and inspect rocks along the way. Some rocks that show signs of containing gems can be broken with a crack hammer or sledgehammer. Be careful not to tunnel into a slope, as the overlying soil and rocks will eventually collapse without warning.

Combination Sites

Many collecting sites consist of a combination of environments. One example is Corundum Knob on Chunky Gal Mountain in Clay County. Combination sites are generally the most physically and technically challenging and often require every rockhounding tool in your arsenal. Sometimes it is necessary to start with a pick and shovel, digging down through many feet of dirt to the hard rock containing the gems. Once you reach the rock, you will have to employ all the hard-rock mining techniques discussed earlier to recover the goodies. As you dig,

Rock screen or sifter

remember that it is especially difficult to perform hard-rock mining at the bottom of a six-foot hole. The larger you make the hole, the easier it will be to work the rock at the bottom. It is not at all uncommon for a rockhound to dig for days just to reach hard rock that may contain gems.

Finding the Tools

Most rockhounding tools can be purchased at large chain hardware stores including Lowe's and Home Depot. You'll find a wide assortment of hammers, chisels, shovels, crowbars, prybars, safety glasses, and work gloves. A rock screen and sifter like the one pictured at left can be easily and inexpensively made from materials also purchased from the hardware store. Other more specialized equipment such as longer chisels, geopicks, gad prybars, and rock hammers can be purchased via the internet at scientific supply companies. The web addresses for some of these companies are as follows:

www.contractorstools.com
www.ascscientific.com
www.jaderockshop.com

Rock hammer

www.legend-reno.com
www.jbfc.com

The finest digger/prybar I have ever used was made in Mt. Ida, Arkansas, for use by professional quartz miners. I have yet to see this tool sold anywhere other than Mt. Ida. You can purchase it over the internet at www.judyscrystals.com.

Gad prybar

Conduct in the Field

Common courtesy and good manners are as important in the field as any equipment. Too many sites still bursting with minerals have been closed forever because of the irresponsibility of just one person. A collector would do well to adhere to the following Code of Ethics established by the American Federation of Mineral Societies:

Code of Ethics

1. I will respect both private and public property and will do no collecting on privately owned land without the owner's permission.
2. I will keep informed on all laws, regulations or rules governing collecting on public lands, and will observe them.
3. I will, to the best of my ability, ascertain the boundary lines of property on which I plan to collect.
4. I will use no firearms or blasting material in collecting areas.
5. I will cause no willful damage to property of any kind—fences, signs, buildings, etc.
6. I will build fires in designated or safe places only and will be certain they are completely extinguished before leaving the area.
7. I will discard no burning material—matches, cigarettes, etc.
8. I will fill all excavation holes which may be dangerous to livestock.
9. I will not contaminate wells, creeks, or other water supply.
10. I will cause no willful damage to collecting material and will take home only what I can reasonably use.
11. I will support the rockhound project H.E.L.P. (Help Eliminate Litter Please) and will leave all collecting areas devoid of litter, regardless of how found.
12. I will cooperate with field trip leaders and those in designated authority in all collecting areas.
13. I will report to my club or federation officers, Bureau of Land Management, or other proper authorities, any deposit of petrified wood or other material on public lands which should be protected for the enjoyment of future generations for public educational and scientific purposes.
14. I will appreciate and protect our heritage of natural resources.
15. I will observe the "Golden Rule," will use "Good Outdoor Manners" and will at all times conduct myself in a manner which will add to the public stature and "Public Image" of rockhounds everywhere.

Permission To Collect

It is impossible to overstate the importance of obtaining permission to enter private property to collect rocks. Too many collecting sites have been closed forever by angry landowners because negligent rockhounds chose to dig on their properties without permission. How would you react if you looked out your window and saw someone digging a hole in your front lawn? **YOU MUST OBTAIN PERMISSION TO ACCESS ANY SITE LOCATED ON PRIVATE PROPERTY. PLEASE GET PERMISSION BEFORE YOU ENTER AND DIG!**

Property access and ownership can change at the mere stroke of a pen or whim of a landowner. Therefore, except for a few sites, no ownership information is provided in this book. However, permission to enter a property should always be secured prior to any collecting trip. Be prepared to track down the owner of a property by knocking on a few doors in the vicinity or by visiting the county courthouse for records. Take time to visit with a property owner to gain his trust. Talk about the weather, his livestock, his family, your family, or any other small talk that comes to mind. It's a good idea to talk as long as the owner seems interested before you ask for permission to access his property to collect.

If the owner is a commercial enterprise, a brief safety training session may be required, and/or a waiver may need to be signed before permission is granted. If it appears that an owner is reluctant to grant permission, it may be prudent to offer some money for the privilege to collect. But be careful—offering money is construed by some to be an insult. Sensitivity to the varieties of human psychology is a real plus in conducting some of the more delicate negotiations.

Safety

The sole intent of this book is to provide information about certain mineral-collecting sites, including the types of rocks and minerals that may be found there. Be advised that rock and mineral collecting is intrinsically dangerous. This book makes no representation that the mineral-collecting locations listed in this book are safe. The author does not encourage anyone to take any risk, whether intentional or unintentional. Each collector should become familiar with all potential hazards of a site and take all appropriate precautions while collecting. In short, it is up to ***you*** to assume sole responsibility for your own safety.

Avery County

Entrance to the Cranberry Iron Mine

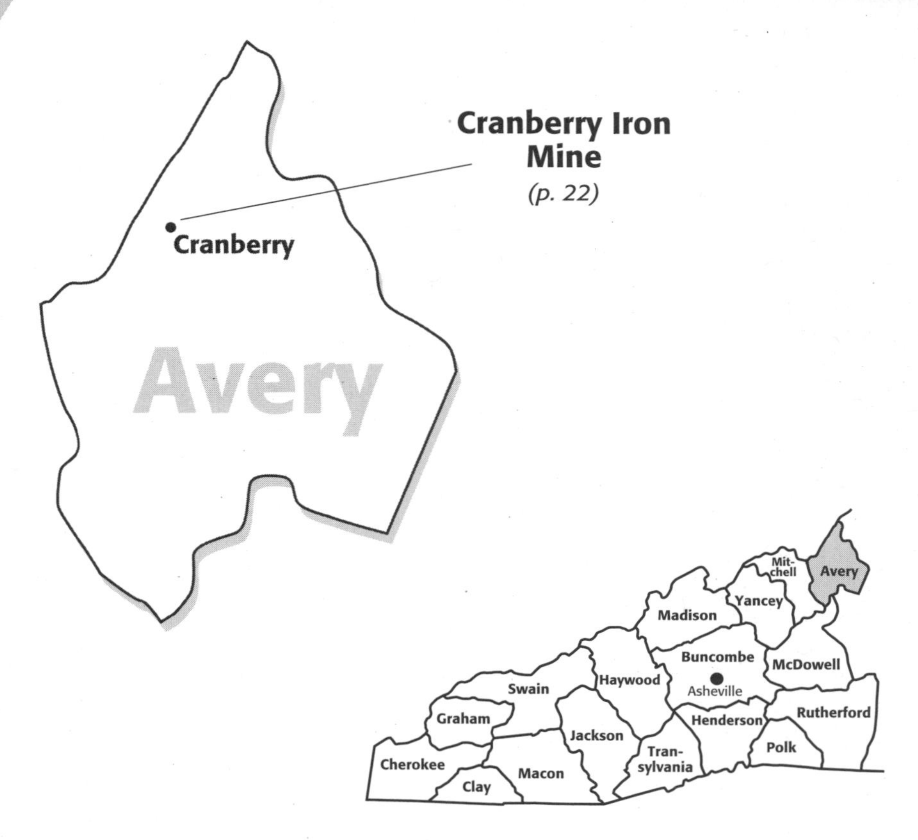

Cranberry Iron Mine

Minerals:
magnetite, epidote, calcite, pyrite, hedenbergite, garnet, pink orthoclase

The history of the Cranberry Iron Mine can be traced back to 1780 when one Reuben White took out a 110-acre land grant. In 1820 production at the mine began, with ore reduced in a Catalan forge. In 1876, the mine was acquired by the Cranberry Iron and Coal Company, which operated systematic mining there until 1927. A narrow-gauge railroad was constructed in 1882 to carry ore between the mine and the Cranberry Iron Works in Johnson City, Tennessee (Stuckey 1965). The building foundations are all that remain of the mill operations. Cavernous mine workings extend approximately 2,500 lateral ft. into the mountainside. Multiple levels with huge rooms are connected to the main adit by ramps and passageways. Veins containing the magnetite ore are made up of banded mixtures of pink and white pegmatite, emerald green epidote gneisses, dark green hornblende, and charcoal gray magnetite. This banded rock is a renowned lapidary material for making unique and striking cabochons. Small pockets containing pyrite and/or white calcite can be found by breaking larger rocks with calcite and pyrite veining. All the rock types and minerals can also be found outside in the mine tailings, so venturing into mine is not mandatory for successful collecting at this location.

Above: Magnetite, calcite, pyrite, and hedenbergite
Below: Magnetite-epidote-feldspar rock

Great care should be taken by anyone entering this mine, as a person could easily become disoriented and get lost or even killed. Along with hammers and chisels, a reliable, high-powered flashlight with at least one backup and extra batteries is a must.

Latitude & Longitude:

36° -08′-22.84″N
81° -58′-19.76″W

Elevation:

3,249 ft

(from Elk Park Quadrangle)

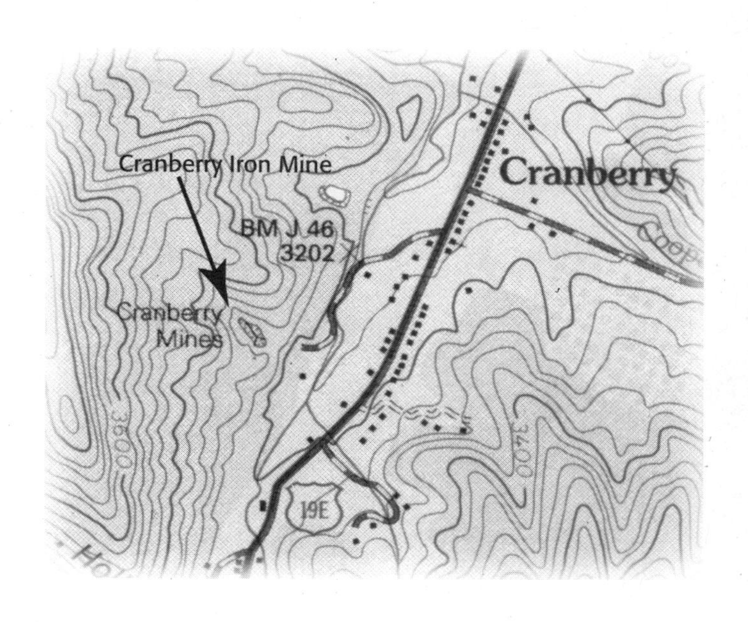

194
Banner Elk
19E
Elk Park
Cranberry
194
topo detail
★=Collecting Area
19E
181

Directions:

From the intersection of Hwy. 19E and Hwy. 194 at Elk Park, drive 0.8 mile south on Hwy. 19E. Turn right (west) on a dirt road and drive 0.25 mile to old building foundations. The mine adits are located about 300 ft. west of these ruins.

Equipment & Tools:

crack hammer, gad point, flat chisels, scratching tools, lantern, flashlight with backup and extra batteries

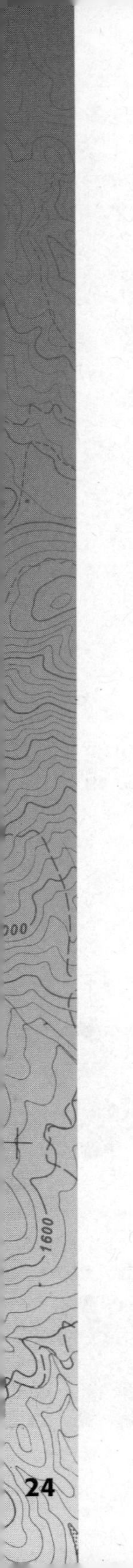

Buncombe County

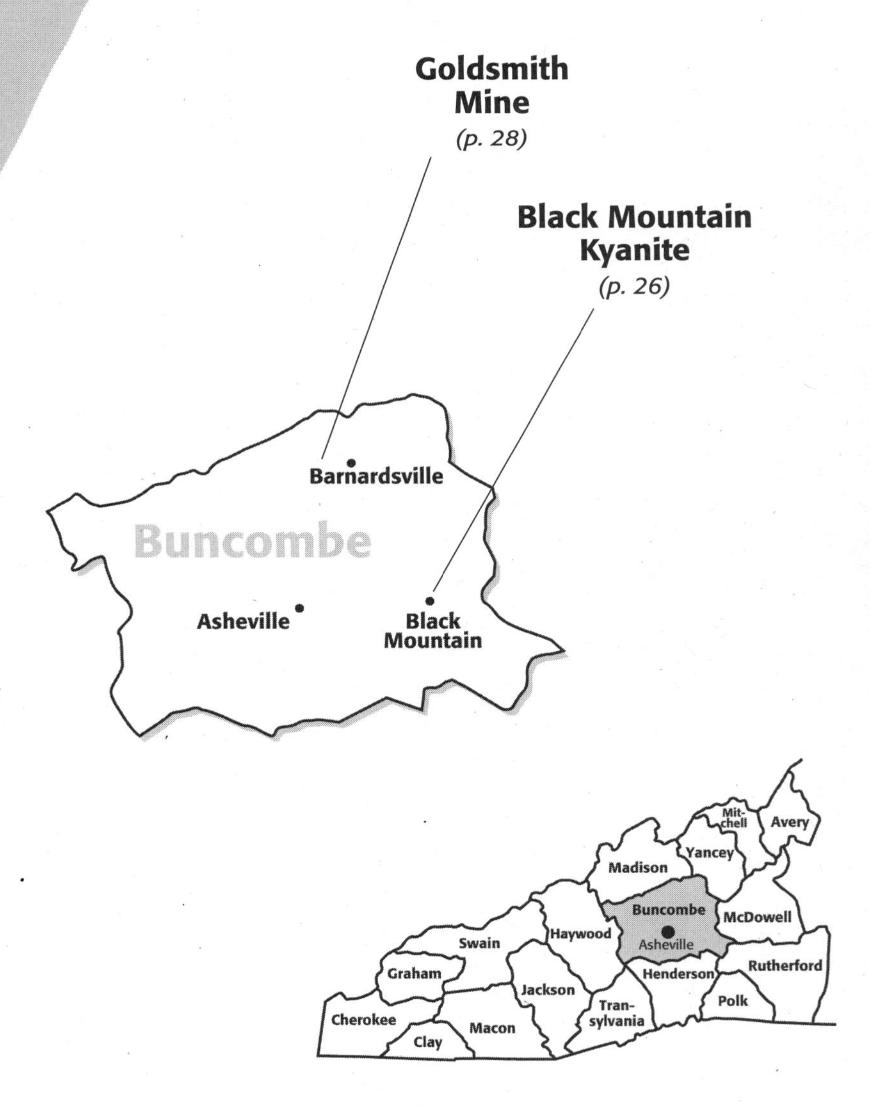

Goldsmith
Mine
(p. 28)
Black Mountain
Kyanite
(p. 26)
Barnardsville
Buncombe
Asheville
Black
Mountain
Mit-
chell
Avery
Yancey
Madison
Buncombe
Asheville
McDowell
Haywood
Swain
Graham
Jackson
Henderson
Rutherford
Polk
Tran-
sylvania
Cherokee
Macon
Clay

Black Mountain Kyanite

Minerals:
kyanite, corundum

A 6- to 8-mile-wide zone of kyanite-bearing gneisses and schists extends for approximately 30 miles from Burnsville in Yancey County to Black Mountain in Buncombe County. Throughout this zone kyanite can also be found in pegmatite dikes and quartz veins. Some of these lenses are composed of pure kyanite. In the Black Mountain area, kyanite-bearing rocks may be found as scattered float material in the stream and surrounding forests, pastures, and residential backyards of McCoy Cove. Large rocks containing light kyanite blades up to 6 in. long and 2 in. wide have been found at this location. Small (generally less than 0.25 in. wide) corundum crystals can occasionally be found within the kyanite matrix.

Kyanite

As you make your way downstream, you may be fortunate enough to come across a fellow rockhound and friend of mine. Major Del Collins (U.S. Army-retired) and his wife Charlotte own a home and a parcel of land adjacent to the stream. Perhaps Major Collins will let you take a few whacks at a huge, incredibly hard kyanite boulder on his property that he has been beating on for way too long now.

Latitude & Longitude:
35° -37′-41.63″N
82° -18′-06.76″W

Elevation:
2,509 ft

(from Montreat Quadrangle)

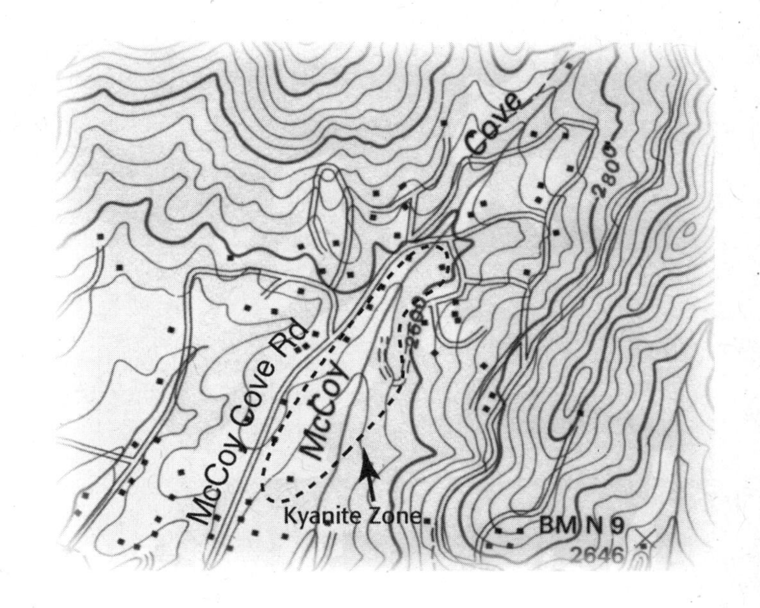

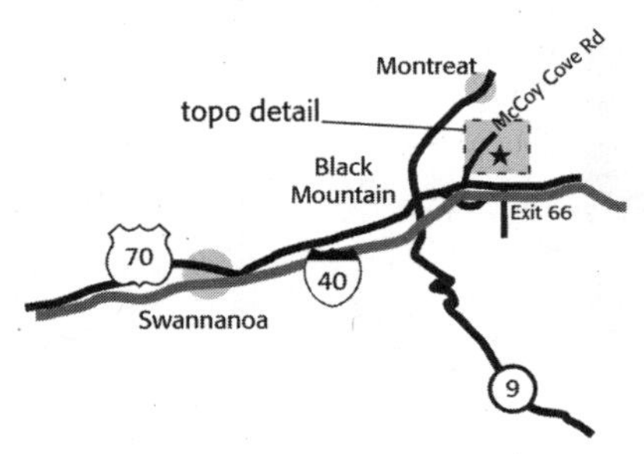

Directions:

Take exit 66 off I-40. Go a short distance on Dunsmore Ave. To Hwy. 70. Turn left (west), and drive 1.1 miles and turn right on McCoy Cove Rd. Drive approximately 0.9 mile to Deer Run Rd. Proceed through a tall rock archway and drive 0.2 mile. Turn right on Melanie Dr. Drive 200 ft. and park. Walk downstream from where the creek crosses the road for about 0.75 mile, looking on both sides for kyanite as you go.

Equipment & Tools:

rock pick, mattock, crack hammer, gad point, flat chisels

Goldsmith Mine

Rocks & Minerals:
white feldspar, moonstone, chalcedony, garnet, olivine, serpentine, chromite, vermiculite

The Allegro Goldsmith mine was mined for feldspar between 1900 and 1935 by the Blue Ridge Mining Company, which leased the property (Hunter and Mattocks 1935). A cut approximately 200 ft. by 35 ft. remains back in the woods. The Goldsmith mine is one of the few pegmatites in the Democrat district to carry white mica (Merschat 1993). The pegmatite is also unique, as it is in contact with a dunite body containing olivine and small black chromite crystals. Partially weathered feldspar veins in the dunite contain small pockets lined with botryoidal chalcedony.

Chromite in peridotite

Chalcedony in feldspar

Latitude & Longitude:
35° -47′-09.00″N
82° -29′-52.89W

Elevation:
2,130 ft

(from Barnardsville Quadrangle)

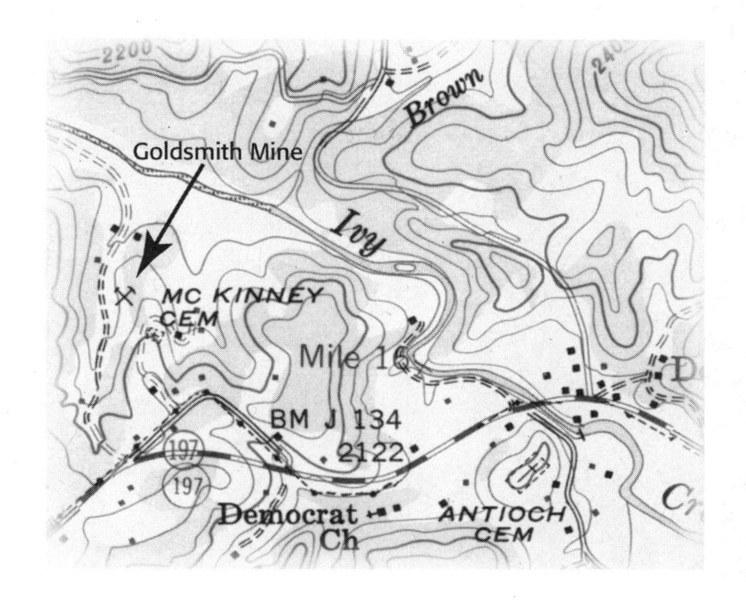

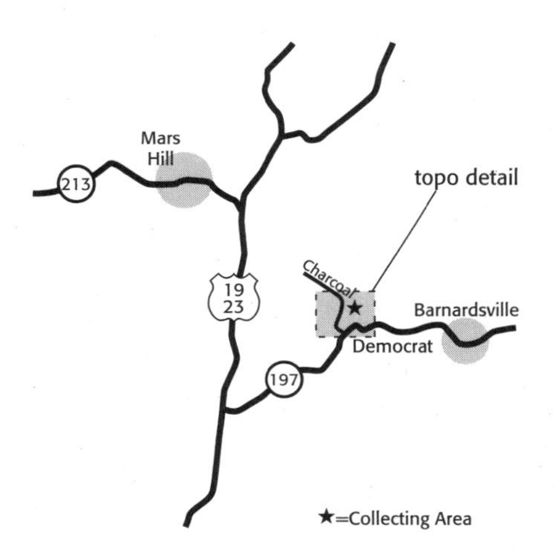

Directions:
From the intersection of Hwy. 19/23 and Hwy. 197, drive 3.6 miles east-northeast to Charcoal Rd. Turn left (north) and drive 0.25 mile, and park on the right side of the road. The mine workings extend primarily in a north-south direction on the east side of Charcoal Rd.

Equipment & Tools:
rock pick, mattock, crack hammer, gad point, flat chisels

2000
1600

Cherokee County

Hitchcock Mine garage, with fire and dump trucks, still standing near Murphy.

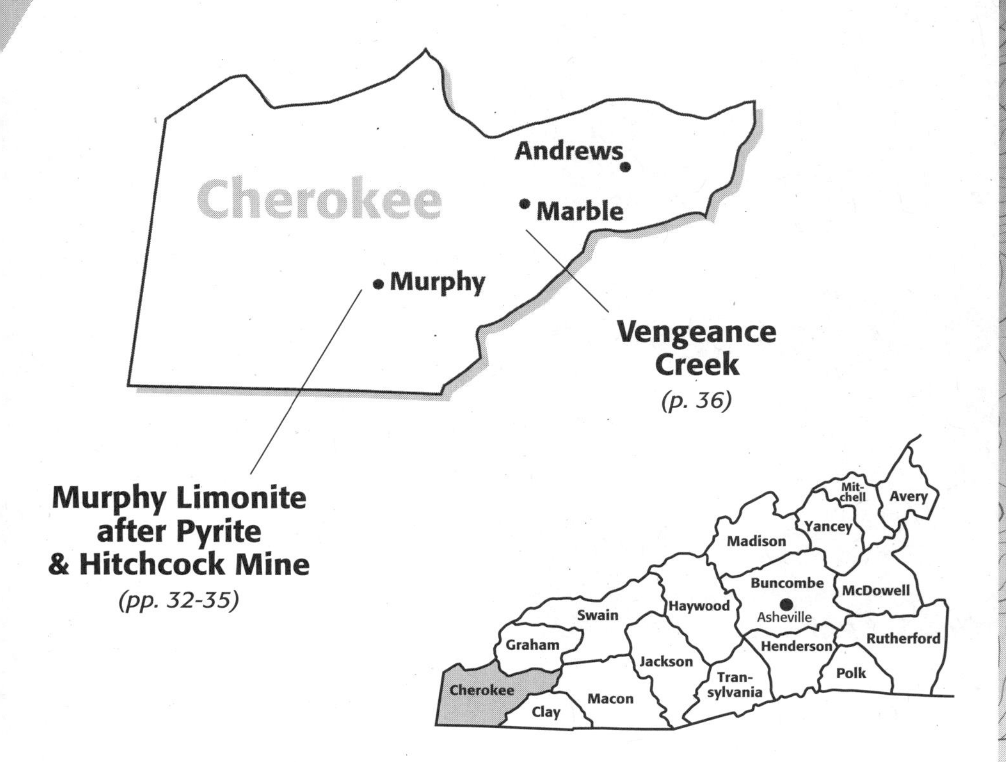

Hitchcock Mine

Rocks & Minerals:
pale green, white, gray, and white talc; tremolite; actinolite; marble; dravite; and tourmaline

The Hitchcock Mine (also known as the Nancy Jordan Mine) is one in a series of talc and marble mines in the Murphy Marble Belt that extends about 50 miles from North Carolina into north Georgia. Operations to produce talc for crayons, cosmetics, textile bleacheries, and rice-polishing material began at the Hitchcock Mine in 1941 when two vertical shafts were driven to approximately 200 ft. below land surface. By the early 1960s, the mine could no longer produce competitive quantities of material and was forced to cease operations. The decaying mine buildings are still standing, and a wide assortment of old trucks and other rusted mining equipment can be found scattered throughout the forest.

Minerals may be found by digging and scratching into old tailings that are heavily overgrown with foliage, including profuse poison ivy in the summer. A new housing development currently being built in the area may soon bring an end to rock collecting in this location.

Above: White talc
Below: Zebra talc

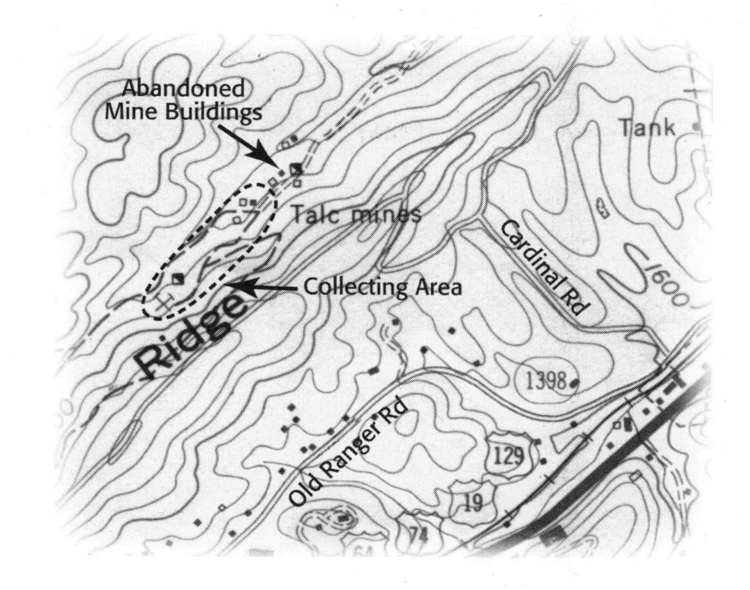

Latitude & Longitude:
35° -04'-46.15"N
84° -03'-13.94"W

Elevation:
1,717 ft

(from Murphy Quadrangle)

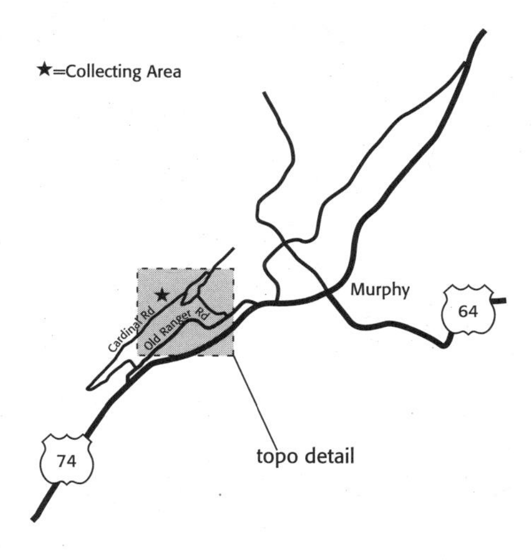

Directions:
From the intersection of Old Ranger Rd. and Cardinal Rd. in Murphy, drive about 0.9 mile on Cardinal Rd. as it twists and turns from northwest to southwest. Park on the side of the road on Fence Ridge and walk northwest about 0.25 mile down the steep slope to the mine workings that extend for approximately 0.50 mile along the lower southeastern slopes.

Equipment & Tools:
rock pick, mattock, shovel, crack hammer, gad point, flat chisels

Murphy Limonite after Pyrite

Minerals:
limonite pseudomorphs after pyrite

Limonite pseudomorphs after pyrite can be found at random within and beneath an eroded, gravelly clay soil bank at the rear of the Citgo service station in west Murphy. Any digging at this location is strictly forbidden, as this would add to the further destabilization of the eroded bank behind the store.

Limonite after pyrite

The limonite cubes and rectangles were formed many millions of years ago as a different mineral called pyrite. After eons of being buried in and beneath iron-rich rocks and soils, there was a gradual removal of the original chemical composition of the pyrite with a corresponding and simultaneous replacement of it by another (limonite). The pyrite crystals, made up of iron and sulfur, have been transformed into limonite, composed of iron oxide and water.

Even though the chemical composition has changed, the original crystal forms of the pyrite have been wonderfully preserved. The resulting crystal is a "pseudomorph" called "limonite after pyrite." It is common to find a limonite after pyrite cube that still contains some pyrite in its core, thus proving its original chemical composition.

Latitude & Longitude:
35° -04'-47.56"N
84° 02'-07.41"W

Elevation:
1,561 ft

(from Murphy Quadrangle)

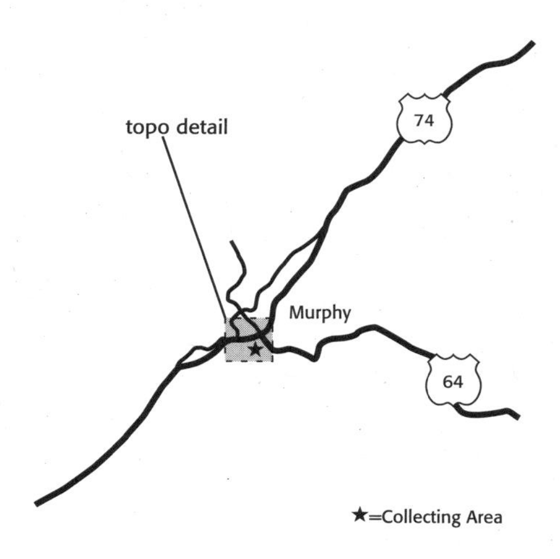

Directions:
Behind the Citgo service station and Subway restaurant near the intersection of Hwy. 19 and Bus. 19 in west Murphy.

Equipment & Tools:
no tools allowed

Vengeance Creek

Minerals:
staurolite

Partially weathered staurolite crystals can be found by screening the gravel in Vengeance Creek. Nearly all the staurolite crystals found at this location are single blades, but the lucky collector can sometimes find twin crystals.

The loose staurolite crystals found in several area creeks have been eroded from ancient metamorphic rocks. The staurolite-containing rock formation extends over a wide area from western North Carolina into northwest Georgia. In fact, even though it is outside the geographical scope of this book, it should be noted that world-class staurolite crystals can be collected at the Hackney Farm near Blue Ridge, Georgia. Information regarding this commercial collecting location can be obtained from the Georgia Mineral Society's Internet web site at www.gamineral.org/commercial-hackney.htm.

Staurolite crystals

Latitude & Longitude:

35° -09′-32.23″N
83° -55′-05.22″W

Elevation:

1,670 ft

(from Marble Quadrangle)

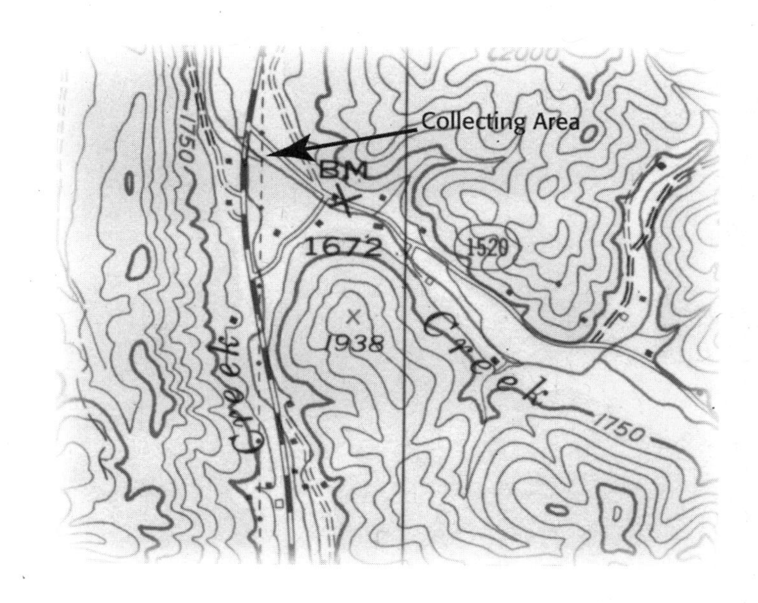

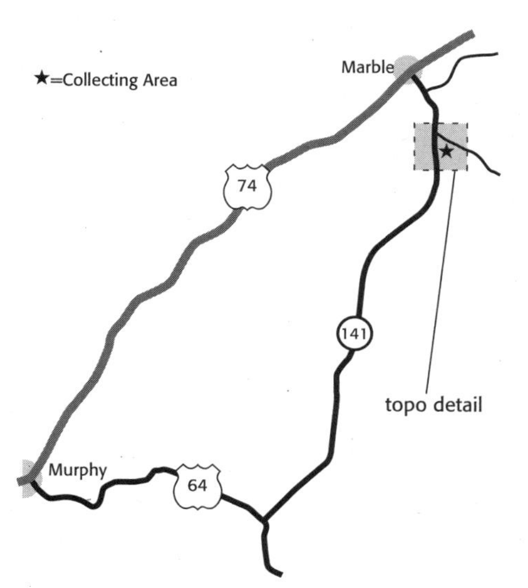

Directions:

From the intersection of Hwy. 19 and Hwy. 141 in Marble, drive 1.1 miles south on Hwy. 141 to SR 1520 (Vengeance Creek Rd.). Turn left (east) and park. Proceed on foot to the creek, located just south of the road, to collect.

Equipment & Tools:

shovel, quarter-inch mesh screen, rubber boots

2000
1600

Clay County

Corundum Knob is covered with broken rock scattered virtually everywhere

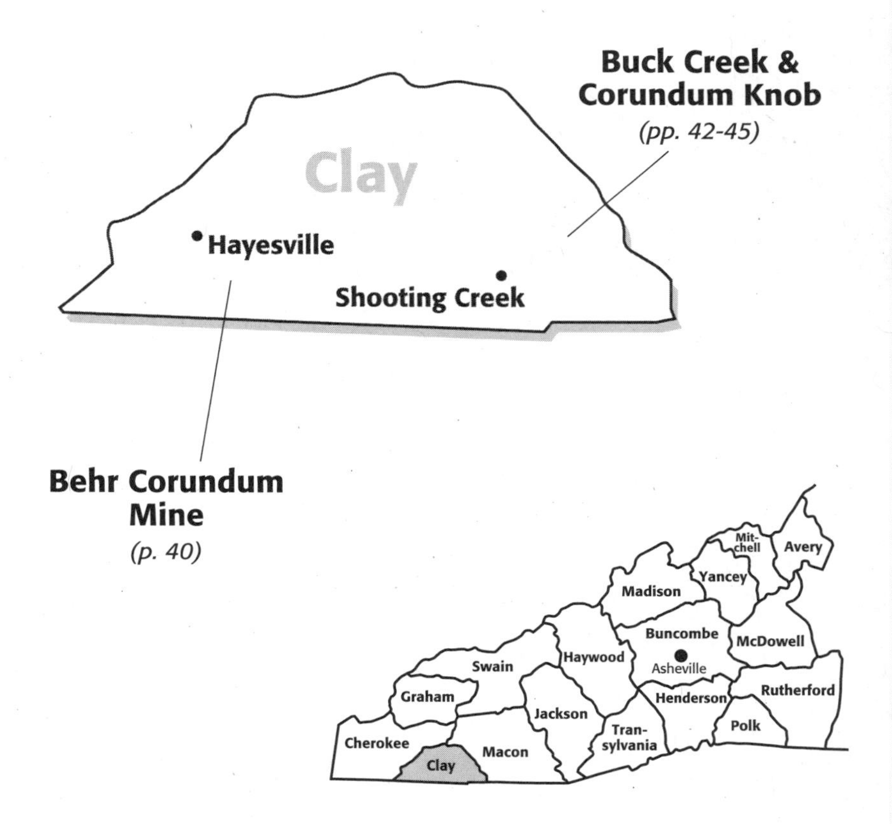

Behr Corundum Mine

Minerals:
sapphire, ruby,
white and gray corundum,
rutile, and hematite

The Behr Corundum Mine was opened in 1880 by Dr. H. S. Lucas, but was soon bought by Herman Behr & Company of New York. The mine's close proximity to Shooting Creek necessitated the constant use of pumps for dewatering. In addition, the nearest shipping point was 25 miles away. These two factors significantly limited the mine's productivity. Upon its closing in 1890, a total of only three carloads of cleaned corundum were reported to have ever been produced and shipped (Pratt and Lewis 1905).

Ruby and sapphire

All that remains today of the mine is a vertical shaft, covered for most of the year by Lake Chatuge. The water-filled shaft is visible only during the winter months when the lake level is low. Corundum can best be found by screening the gravel in the vicinity of the mineshaft. Corundum can also be found by surface collecting along the shoreline of Lake Chatuge.

Latitude & Longitude:

35° -01′-28.94″N
83° -44′-25.24″W

Elevation:

1,925 ft

(from Shooting Creek Quadrangle)

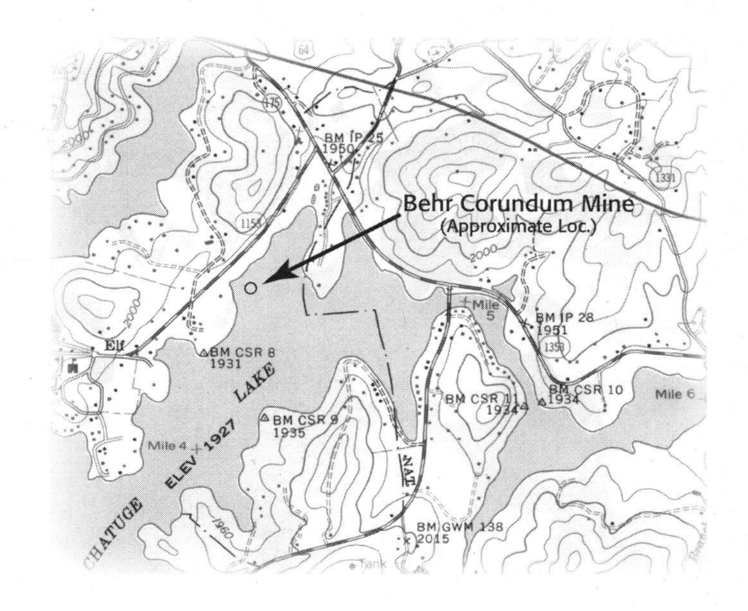

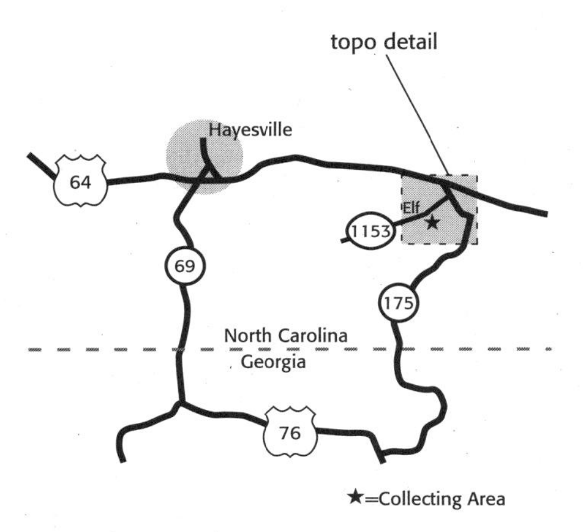

Directions:

From Hwy. 64 at the North Shores of Lake Chatuge, drive 0.4 mile south on Hwy. 175 and turn right (southwest) on SR 1153 toward Elf. Drive another 0.4 mile, park on the side of the road, and walk a short distance to the shoreline. The mine appears, as a water-filled hole, only when the lake level is low.

Equipment & Tools:

shovel, mattock, quarter-inch mesh screen, rubber boots

Buck Creek

Minerals:
almandine garnet, corundum

Buck Creek is located about 0.5 mile east (running generally from south to north) of Corundum Knob, so much of what is written about that area (p. 44) also pertains to this location. Small (generally less than an eighth-inch), water-worn chips of dark red, cuttable almandine garnet can be screened from the gravels in Buck Creek. The best place to screen the creek's gravel for garnet is just north of the bridge. Corundum can be found by screening about 0.4 mile north of the bridge, below and to the north of the former Big Shaft location. Another screening location for corundum is in the creek below the old Herbert Mine. You can get to the old Herbert Mine by driving 1.3 miles north from the Buck Creek bridge and walking about 0.6 mile west on a road/trail to an unnamed creek just west of Fishprong Branch. Dunite and serpentine can also be collected by driving 0.4 mile north from the bridge and hiking southwest less than 0.5 mile uphill along a small, intermittent stream.

Above: Almandine garnet fragments
Below: Corundum in matrix and pieces (front)

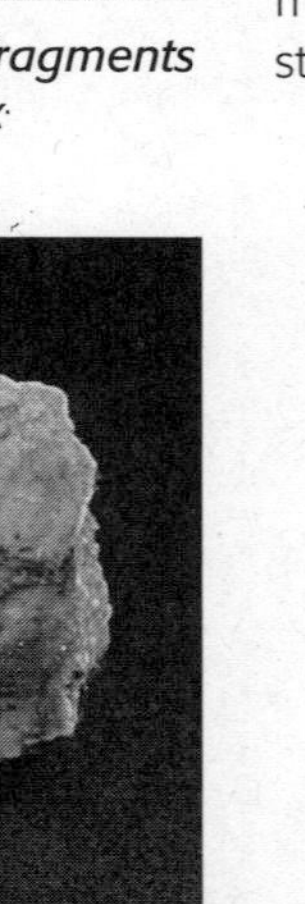

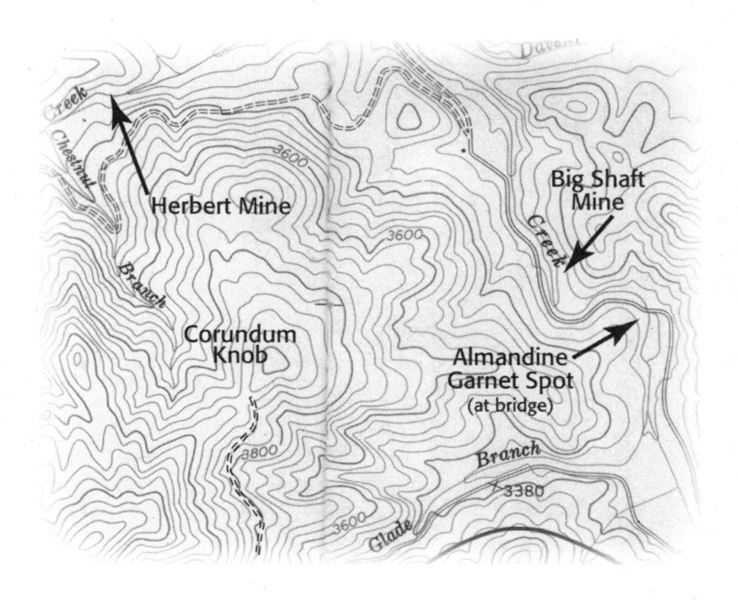

Latitude & Longitude:

35° -05'-00.74"N
83° -36'-46.78"W

Elevation:

3,310 ft

(from Rainbow Springs and Shooting Creek Quadrangles)

Directions:

Drive 1.4 miles east on Hwy. 64 from Glade Gap and turn left onto Buck Creek Rd. Drive 0.8 mile north on Buck Creek Rd. to a bridge over the creek.

Equipment & Tools:

shovel, eighth-inch mesh screen for corundum, sixteenth-inch mesh screen or smaller for garnet, rubber boots

Portal to Big Shaft Mine near Buck Creek

Corundum Knob

Minerals:
ruby, sapphire, corundum, olivine, edenite, feldspar, zoisite, serpentine minerals

Corundum Knob is aptly named. Corundum deposits in dunite and associated rocks have been worked here since 1875. From 1878 until 1900, the mines in this area, along with those in north Georgia, were the world's only large-scale abrasive corundum producers. Although production from these deposits had ceased by 1906, they helped to establish corundum as an American industry for the first two decades of the 20th century. The corundum deposits were investigated by the U.S. Geological Survey to determine whether they would help to relieve the critical shortage of abrasive needed in war industries (they would not) (Hadley 1949). The numerous cuts made by the USGS can still be found around Corundum Knob.

The main dunite body making up most of Corundum Knob occupies nearly half a square mile. Within the dunite are lense-like bodies of troctolite as large as 70 ft. wide by 1,500 feet long. Troctolite is composed of olivine with varying amounts of calcic plagioclase feldspar with secondary enstatite, amphibolite, chlorite-amphibole schist, or chlorite-olivine-serpentine rock (Hadley 1949). Gray corundum with hints of pink and blue can be found in pods or isolated grains in the troctolite. Small, blood-red ruby crystals can be found widely disseminated in a beautiful pale green to emerald green rock called smaragdite which is composed of mostly olivine, calcic plagioclase, and aluminous amphibole (edenite). A sledgehammer is a must for breaking rocks that show hints of ruby on the outside. The emerald green rock with scattered small red rubies makes beautiful cabochons. The flanks of Corundum Knob look as though they have been bombed, with hundreds of holes dug to follow troctolite veins and an untold volume of scattered broken rock. Loose crystals of white, gray, pink, and blue corundum can be found by screening the gravelly soils in and around area creeks. Three noteworthy corundum screening locations are: 1) in the intermittent stream just north of the Cat Eye Cut, 2) in and around Buck Creek especially below the former Big Shaft Mine, and 3) in the stream below the former Herbert Mine (see topo maps, pp. 43 & 45). Although most of the corundum found by screening is in small pieces generally less than a couple of inches wide, there are reports of complete hexagonal crystals up to 6 in. long and 4 in. wide.

Ruby in edenite-amphibolite

Latitude & Longitude:

35° -04'-53.26"N
83° -37'-37.46"W

Elevation:

4,012 ft

(from Rainbow Springs and Shooting Creek Quadrangles)

topo detail
Glade Branch
Buck Cr Rd
to Franklin
Glade Gap
64
★=Collecting Area
to Hayesville

Directions:

At about 0.2 miles northeast of Glade Gap on Hwy. 64, go north on paved road that goes to Glade Branch. At about 50 yd. take the left fork onto a dirt and gravel Forest Service road. Drive about 1 mile to parking area in front of a Forest Service bulletin board. Hike the trail east about 0.25 mile past Corundum Knob to the main smaragdite-collecting locality. Old diggings and broken rock containing corundum may be found by hiking along the south, east, and north flanks of Corundum Knob. A hard-to-follow trail goes north along the east flank of Corundum Knob to an intermittent stream below the Cat Eye Cut (see details on p. 44).

Equipment & Tools:

sledgehammer, rock pick, mattock, shovel, crack hammer, gad point, flat chisels, quarter-inch mesh screen, rubber boots (to wear while screening)

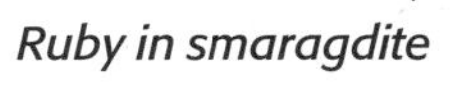

Ruby in smaragdite

Haywood County

Entrance to adit at Haywood County's Redmond Prospect

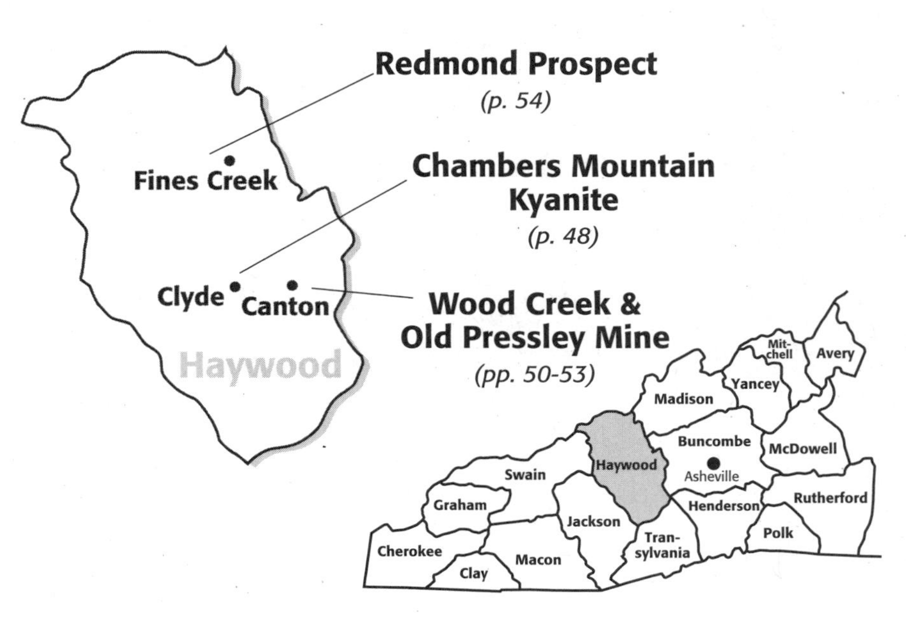

Chambers Mountain Kyanite

Minerals:
kyanite

Rocks composed mostly of pale blue kyanite blades up to 6 in. long and 1.5 in. wide can be found as float material in this general area by walking the pastures and forest. Some pieces that appear coated with brown iron oxide can be successfully cleaned with oxalic acid.

Choose a clear, warm day to visit Chambers Mountain. From the top, and from open pastures on the uppermost southern flanks, you will be rewarded with an unforgettable bird's eye view of the awesome Blue Ridge. You will likely be greeted along the way by harmless cattle that always seem anxious to make sure you aren't a wily coyote attempting to "join" the herd. In a pasture, you can choose one of countless large boulders on which to take a break, bask in the sun, or enjoy your lunch while looking out over a seemingly endless view. Be careful, though—you might find yourself getting so comfortable you'll begin to forget all about kyanite.

Kyanite in matrix

Latitude & Longitude:

35º -33′-55.88″N
82º -54′-39.86″W

Elevation:

3,856 ft

(from Clyde Quadrangle)

topo detail
gravel rd
Chambers Mtn Rd
40
Hyder Mtn Rd
Charles St
Clyde
74
19
★=Collecting Area

Directions:

From Hwy. 19 (Main St.) in Clyde, drive about 0.2 mile north on Charles St. to Hyder Mountain Rd. Turn left (west) and drive 0.4 mile, following the Pigeon River to Chambers Mtn. Rd. Turn right (north) on Chambers Mtn. Rd. Follow the paved road about 1.5 miles and turn left onto a gravel road marked by two green road signs to Chambers Mtn. Fire Tower and Lookout Pt. Follow the gravel road generally northward to a gate. Park at the gate and hike up the road approximately 1 mile to the kyanite-collecting area indicated on the topo map.

Equipment & Tools:

rock pick, mattock, crack hammer, gad point, flat chisels

Wood Creek

Minerals:
corundum (blue, gray, pink, white, and star sapphire)

Wood Creek is located just east and down gradient of the Old Pressley Sapphire Mine, so it contains the same type of material. Blue, gray, pink, white, and clear corundum and star sapphire weathered from pegmatite can be found in alluvial gravels along Wood Creek. Large pieces of opaque and color-zoned corundum up to 30 pounds have been found, although pieces this large are extremely rare. Complete hexagonal crystals are not common but can be found by the lucky collector.

Sapphire

The corundum is mostly concentrated in sporadic alluvial gravel layers from 3 ft. to 9 ft. below grade, so much digging and screening is required to recover the screening material. Screening must be done in the creek located in a horse and cow pasture, making for very dirty work. Collecting results are generally best in the spring and fall when the creek's water volume is sufficient for screening.

There is a fee of $15 per day per person to collect at this location.

Latitude & Longitude:

35° 34'-21.46"N
82°-48'-31.82"W

Elevation:

2,798 ft

(from Canton Quadrangle)

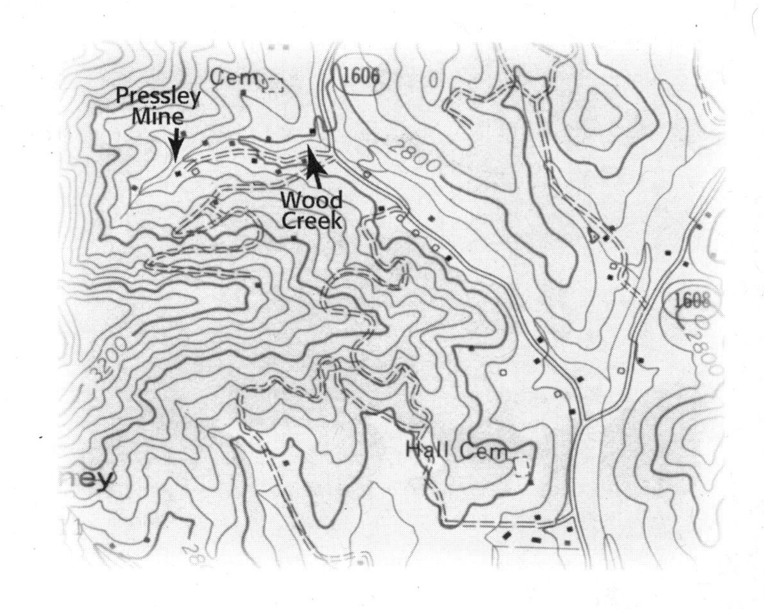

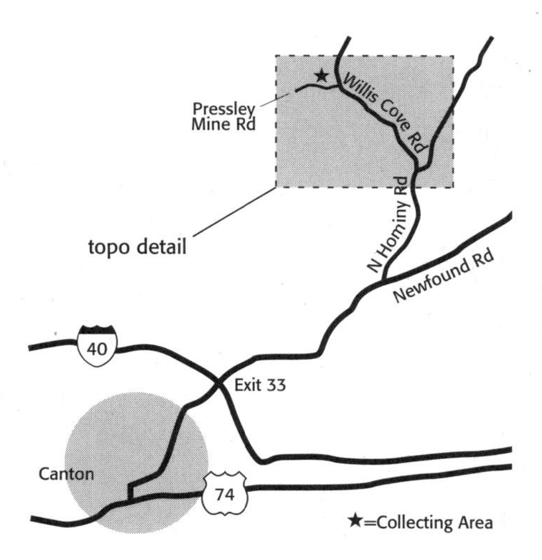

Directions:

From I-40 take exit 33 and drive 1 mile east on Newfound Rd. Turn left (north) on North Hominy Rd. and drive 0.6 mile to Willis Cove Rd. Turn left onto Willis Cove Rd. and drive 0.5 mile to Pressley Mine Rd. on the left. Turn left onto Pressley Mine Rd. The entrance to Wood Creek is about 100 yd. on the right.

Equipment & Tools:

rock pick, mattock, shovel, quarter-inch mesh screen

Old Pressley Sapphire Mine

Minerals:
corundum (blue, gray, white, and star sapphire)

The Old Pressley mine was first worked around 1900, when tunnels and shafts were driven into the mountainside to follow a pegmatite dike containing corundum crystals and pieces up to 5 or 6 in. across. The very large crystal shown below was collected in 2002. The corundum is generally color zoned, varying in hue from silvery gray to deep blue and violet shades and contains much "silk," making it excellent material for cutting brilliant star stones. Many have tried their luck in mining the site over the years, including the current owners, who are attempting to reopen old tunnels and shafts. The mine is the source for the 1,445-carat "Star of the Carolinas," the world's largest star sapphire.

Sapphire crystals

The Old Pressley Mine is a commerical collecting site where buckets of material can be purchased or dug by yourself for a fee. All necessary equipment and materials are furnished, but it might be a good idea to bring your own just in case. A running sluice box with benches makes for easy screening. There is a small rock shop and a picnic area on the property.

Latitude & Longitude:

35° 34'-18.97"N
82° -48'-42.41"W

Elevation:

2,867 ft

(from Canton Quadrangle)

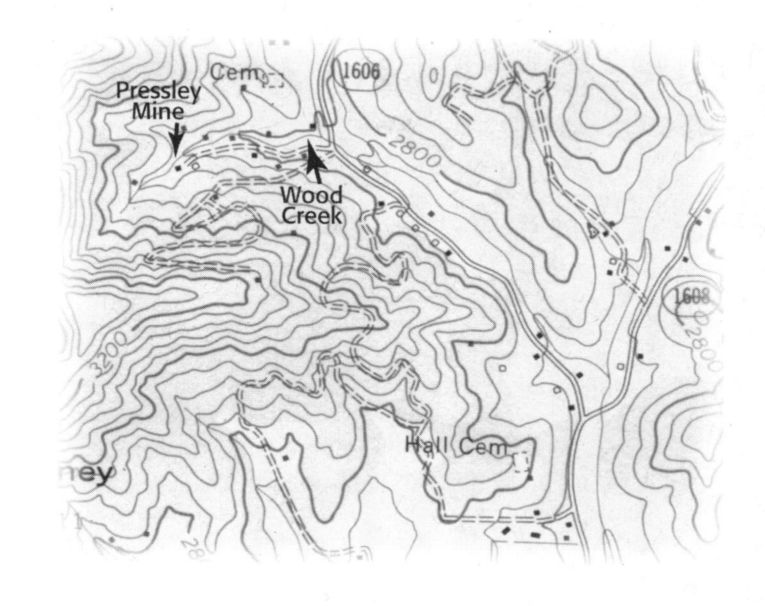

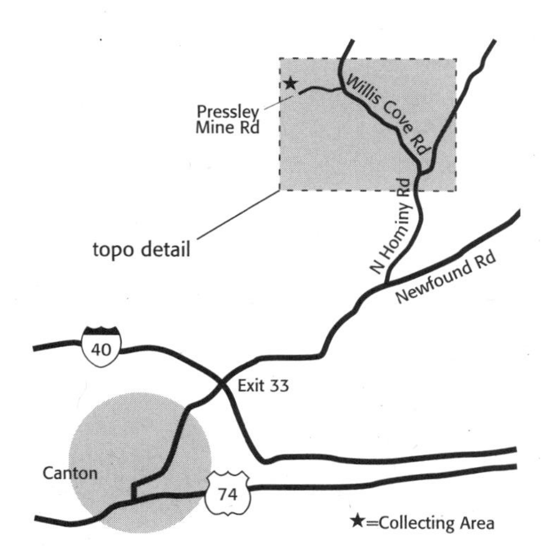

Directions:

From I-40 take exit 33 and drive 1 mile east on Newfound Rd. (SR 1004). Turn left (north) on North Hominy Rd. and drive 0.6 mile to Willis Cove Rd. Turn left onto Willis Cove Rd. and drive 0.5 mile to Pressley Mine Rd. on the left. Turn left onto Pressley Mine Rd. and drive about 0.2 mile west to the rock shop and sluice box.

Equipment & Tools:

rock pick, mattock, shovel

Redmond Prospect

Minerals:
azurite, malachite, chrysocolla, cerussite, pyromorphite, galena, pyrite, sphalerite

In early June 1907, Robert Grab Rathbone was squirrel hunting on the 3,000-acre property of S. M. Redmond near Fines Creek when he caught a glimpse of rusty-colored stones beside a groundhog hole. Rathbone picked up a metallic-looking stone and was surprised by how heavy it was. He took this and other similar rocks to his cousin George Rathbone's forge, where an attempt to melt the material resulted only in some acrid yellow smoke and a few silvery specks on the surface of the blackened rock. Rathbone initially thought that the specks might be silver or at least lead.

The next day Rathbone told Redmond of his find. Together the two men returned to the groundhog hole with pick and shovel. They dug for a day and a half, filling a burlap sack with metallic-looking rock. Several weeks later, Redmond optioned the site to speculators from Newport, Tennessee. The speculators hired Rathbone and his friend Will Parton who blasted and dug through 18 ft. of rock below the groundhog hole. The speculators gave up after a couple of weeks, not knowing they had missed the main vein by just a few feet. For the next 20 years, Rathbone spent many hours digging around the 18-ft. shaft.

Upon his death in 1927, Redmond deeded Rathbone a one-third interest in the mineral deposit. That year, James Atkins of Waynesville and a Mr. Keith from Alabama optioned the site and hired as many as 15 men, including Rathbone as foreman, to prospect the site. An 11-ft.-thick vein with an 8- to 18-inch center of nearly pure galena was discovered. A mining company offered Atkins and Keith $50,000 for the deposit, but they turned it down. In 1937, Cassidy, Harwood, and Patton took out an option on the mine. In all, only one 45-ton carload of lead ore was recovered. This operation proved to be unprofitable, and all attempts to mine the deposit were abandoned. In 1952, George H. Bowman of Elk Park and Hamilton Wood of Hendersonville optioned the mine. Core drilling at the entrance to the horizontal tunnel showed the vein to be 80 ft. deep at that point (Asheville-Citizen Times 1957).

A 150-ft. tunnel, along with some eroded cuts and spoil piles, stands today as a reminder of Rathbone's 100-year-old discovery and all the aborted attempts to mine the deposit. The first 50 ft. of the tunnel is covered year-round by a pool of cold water up to 2 ft. deep. Small crystals of azurite, cerussite, galena, sphalerite, and pyrite can be found by scratching in the spoil piles outside the mine or by working with a crack hammer and chisel inside the mine. Small green pyromorphite crystals can be found by cracking large quartz vein boulders scattered in the spoil piles along the wooded slopes above the mine.

Latitude & Longitude:

35° -40′-54.12″N
83° -00′-56.82″W

Elevation:

2533 ft

(from Cove Creek Gap Quadrangle)

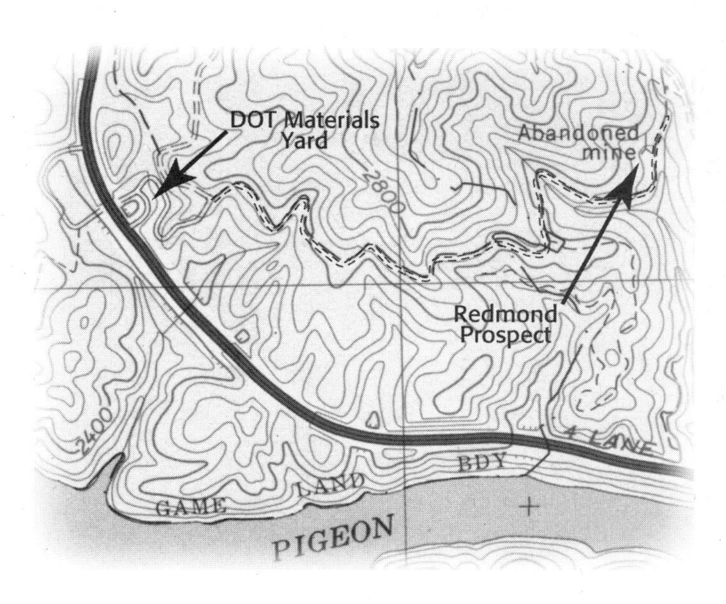

topo detail
Fines Creek
Exit 15
★=Collecting Area
209
40
276
to Waynesville

Directions:

Travel 2.4 miles west on I-40 from the Fines Creek Rd. overpass (exit 15) to the turnout into the N. C. Dept. of Transportation materials yard. Go east on an unmarked dirt and gravel road approximately 1.3 miles to the spoil piles and mine entrance. The last 0.75 mile of the road is rutted, so 4-wheel drive is recommended for dry weather and mandatory for rain or snow. The adit is located on the northwest side of the road, and the majority of spoil piles are located on the southeast side.

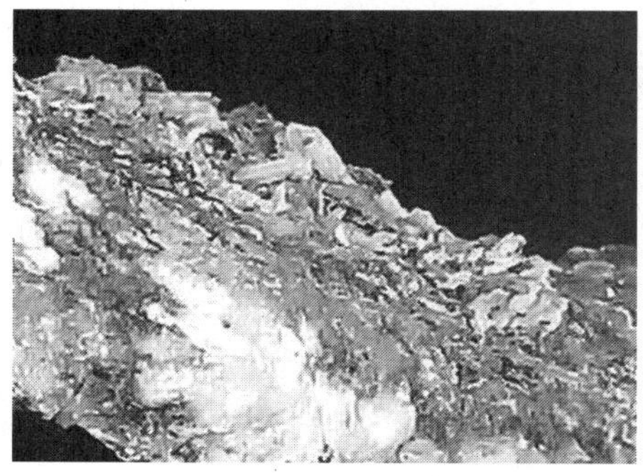

Cerussite and chrysocolla on limonite and quartz

Equipment & Tools:

rock pick, mattock, scratching tools, crack hammer, gad point, flat chisels, prybar, lantern, flashlight with backup and extra batteries, hip waders

Jackson County

Abandoned Ruby City mill foundations still remaining in the forest

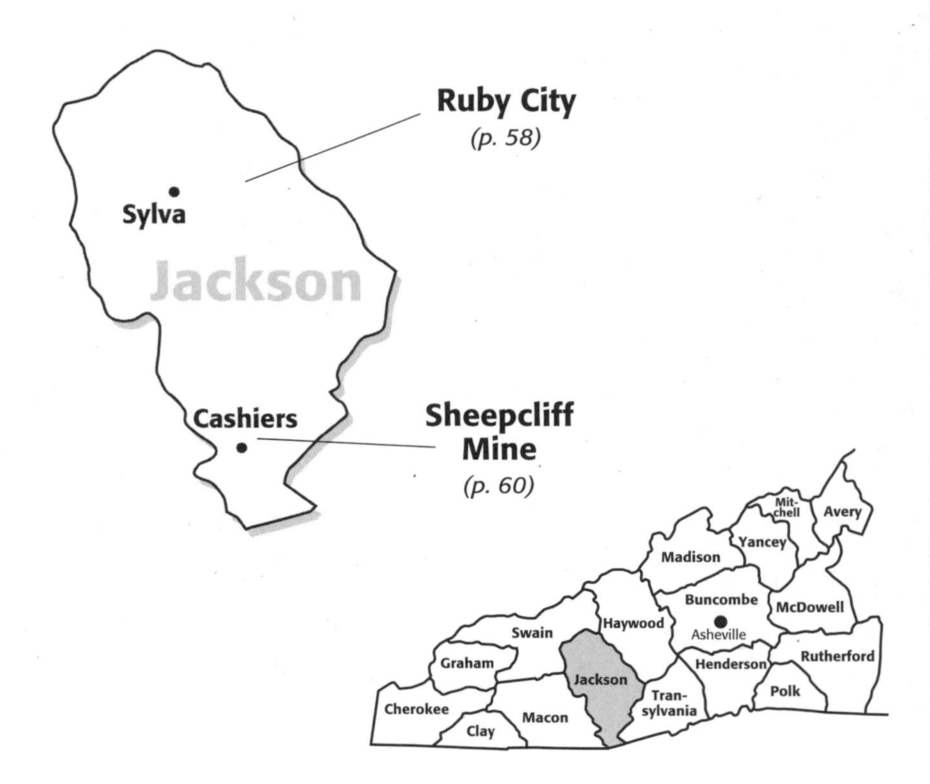

Ruby City

Minerals:
rhodolite garnet in mica schist

The light purple-colored garnet in mica schist found in this area was first mined for abrasives near the turn of the century. A small mill was built on the property to process the ore. The property was acquired in 1923 by the Rhodolite Company of LeRoy, New York, who planned to mine the garnet for abrasive paper (Stuckey 1965). Six hundred thousand dollars were spent constructing a modern mill in 1925, only to have operations cease after just six months because it was discovered that garnet from this area made poor abrasive paper. The "Rho-gar" did not retain the sharp edges required for abrasion (Rankin 1940). A 40-ft. by 50-ft. drift was cut into the side of the mountain 150 ft. west of the South Fork of Sugarloaf Creek.

Rhodolite garnet in schist

A large concrete mill foundation still remains today, tucked away in the forest as a permanent reminder of a long-ago and poorly planned mining scheme. Because the mine was closed on such short notice, more rock was mined than was processed, and there are plenty of spoil piles between the drift and the creek to sort through to find rhodolite garnet-bearing rocks. Crack and sledgehammers are necessary, along with gad points and chisels, to break the larger rocks and boulders down to carrying-size pieces. To help transport your booty back to your vehicle, you might consider bringing in a cart or hand truck and leaving it at the mill foundation while you are mining farther up the trail. I sometimes wonder if my arms have gotten longer from having carried too many 5-gallon buckets full of heavy rocks by hand back to my truck. If that were possible, I'd be dragging my knuckles on the ground by now.

Latitude & Longitude:
35° -22′-34.14″N
83° -07′-04.91″W

Elevation:
3,476 ft

(from Hazelwood Quadrangle)

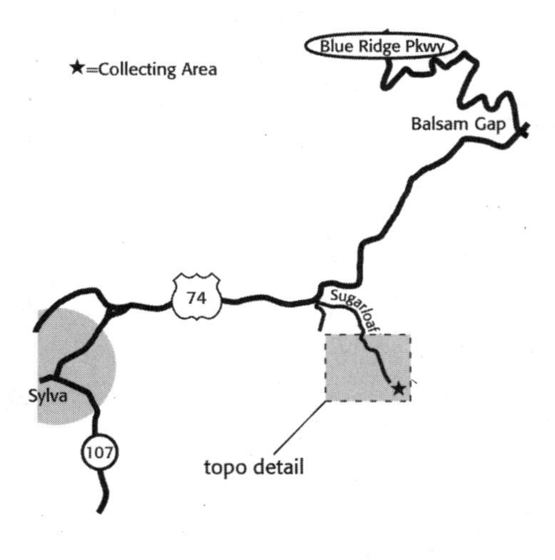

Directions:
From Sylva, drive approximately 4.5 miles east on Hwy. 23/74 to Sugarloaf Rd. on the right. Drive about 1.75 miles south to a Forest Service gate and park. Walk approximately 0.5 miles to the foundations of an old processing mill at "Ruby City." Follow the trail up a steep incline just to the left of the old mill foundations pictured on p. 57, and walk 0.25 miles to a cut located on the right side of the trail.

Equipment & Tools:
rock pick, mattock, crack hammer, sledgehammer, gad point, flat chisels

Sheepcliff Mine

Minerals:
beryl, white and pink feldspar, clear and smoky quartz, mica

Feldspar along with mica and beryl were mined at Sheepcliff in 1942 and again in 1945 or 1946. The workings consist of an open cut approximately 100 ft. long and 70 ft. wide at its widest point. The western edge of the cut extends downward beneath a pool of water (Olson 1952). Yellowish- to bluish-green beryl, massive clear and smoky quartz, and white and pink feldspar can be found by scratching through the spoil piles in and outside the cut. The material may also be screened in the deep pool covering the western edge of the cut. Unfortunately for rockhounds, a resort community is currently being developed in the area that surrounds the mine. Therefore, it is only a matter of time before access to the mine will be prohibited.

Sheepcliff Mine

Latitude & Longitude:
35° -08'-05.55"N
83° -05'-28.40"W

Elevation:
4,123 ft

(from Big Ridge Quadrangle)

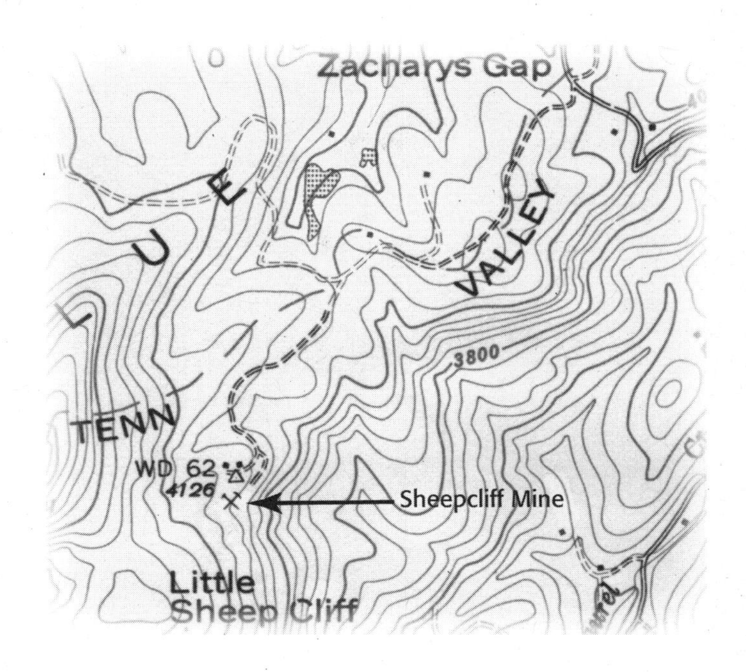

topo detail
Laurel Creek Rd
107
64
Cashiers
★=Collecting Area

Directions:
From the intersection of Hwy. 107 and Hwy. 64 in Cashiers, drive 2.2 miles east on Hwy. 64 to Laurel Creek Rd. Turn left (north) and drive 2.5 miles to Treasurewood Rd. Turn left (west) and drive 1.1 miles and park. The mine is about 250 ft. south of this location. A new housing development in the area may close the site to collectors in the near future.

Equipment & Tools:
rock pick, mattock, shovel,
crack hammer, gad point, flat chisels,
quarter-inch mesh screen

Beryl crystals and pieces

Macon County

Surrounding the town of Franklin in Macon County are numerous commercial gem mines where, for a fee, you can try your luck at finding dark red ruby, beautiful blue sapphire, red pyrope and purple almandine garnet, and other minerals by screening bucketfuls of furnished materials. Almost all of these mines enrich their buckets with native and non-native stones. Since the minerals are furnished in enriched buckets and no actual collecting can be performed, these mines fall outside the scope of this book. However, the mines are worth mentioning as great sources of entertainment for the whole family. A complete list of these gem mines, including pertinent collecting information, is given in the appendix of this book. For additional information, write Franklin Area Chamber of Commerce at 425 Porter Street, Franklin, NC 28734, call them at 800-336-7829, or visit their internet web site at www.franklin-chamber.com.

Corundum mining first took place in Macon County at Corundum Hill in 1871 (Stuckey 1965). In the late 19th and early 20th centuries, Tiffany's of New York, the American Prospecting & Mining Company, and the U.S. Ruby Mining Company all made unsuccessful attempts to find the sources of the ruby and sapphire deposits. The "mother lode" for the alluvial deposits has yet to be found (Franklin Area Chamber of Commerce 2001).

Madison County

Little Pine Garnet Mine, originally mined for abrasives in the early 20th century

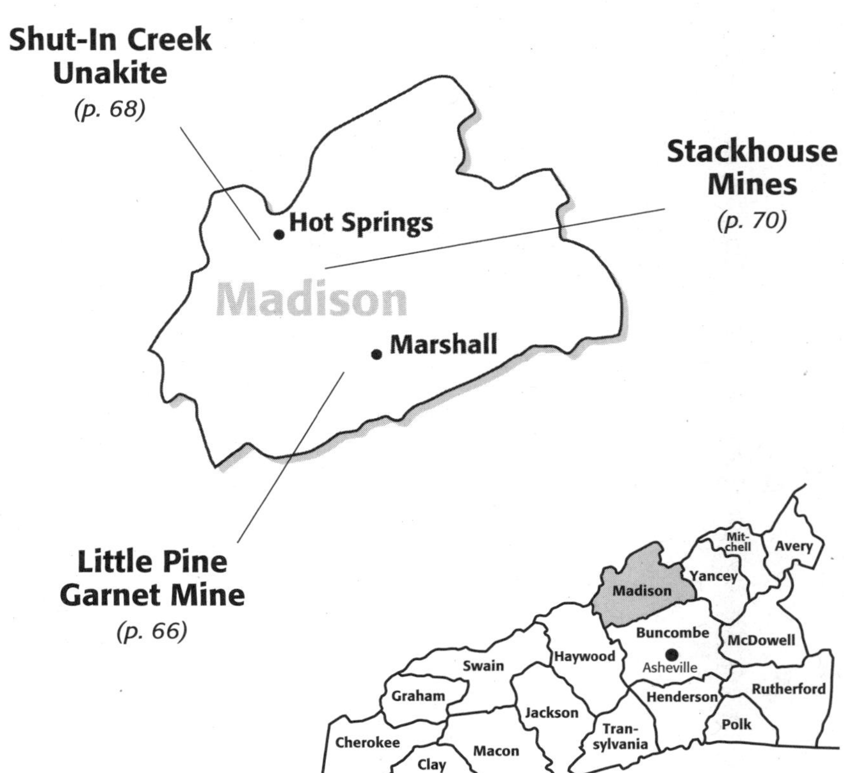

Little Pine Garnet Mine

Minerals:
almandite garnets in chlorite schist

The Little Pine Garnet Mine was mined for abrasives in 1904 and 1905 (Stuckey 1965). An adit extends into the hillside approximately 150 ft. Red almandine garnets up to 6 in. in diameter occur in a green chlorite schist. With some effort and skill, garnets can be plucked from the walls of the adit using a crack hammer and sharp chisel. The adit has three main levels, the lowest being the smallest and shortest, with few large crystals. You will enter the mine on the middle level, where two large pillars of rock have been left to support the roof. The upper level extends the full length of the adit. Most of it is sloped at a treacherous 45-degree angle toward the lower levels. It is best reached via an inclined 4-ft. rise beyond the second pillar. Perch on the narrow paths and landings at the head and foot of the slope while extracting garnets from the walls. Larger crack hammers, chisels, and prybars are useful to bring down garnet-bearing chlorite schist from the walls of the mine. The best specimens are those remaining in the chlorite schist matrix. Nearly all of the garnets have been extensively replaced by chlorite, but an occasional piece of facet-grade material may be found. Despite the chlorite replacement, most garnets found here retain excellent crystal form. Flashlights and lanterns are a must for working inside the adit. A good head-lamp is necessary to keep both your hands free for working.

Above: Garnet in chlorite schist
Below: Almandine garnet crystals

Dig for garnets in the gravelly soils about 600 ft. due south of the adit. Reach the digging site by going straight (southeast) for 200 yd. up a dirt road after driving through the creek. You can also dig in the spoil piles on the slopes across the creek from the adit.

Latitude & Longitude:
35° -46′-13.68″N
82° -44′-15.99″W

Elevation:
1,847 ft

(from Marshall Quadrangle)

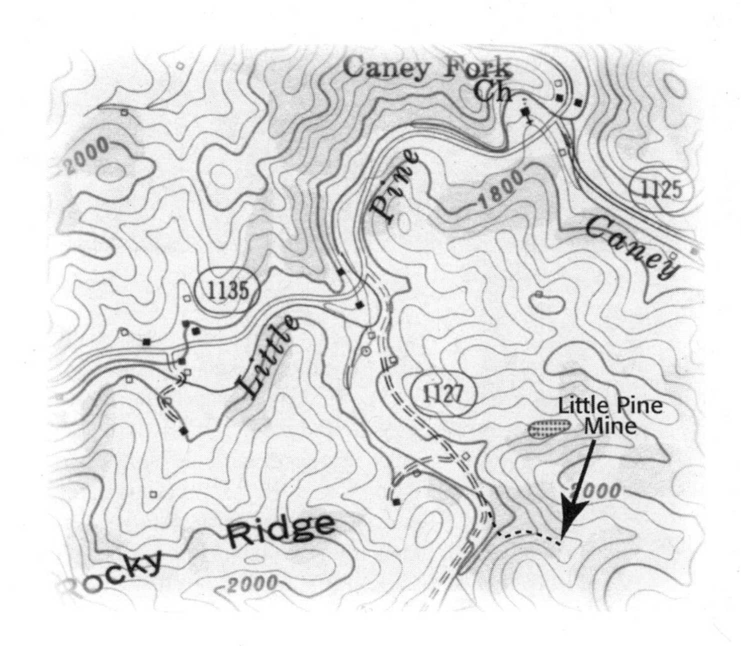

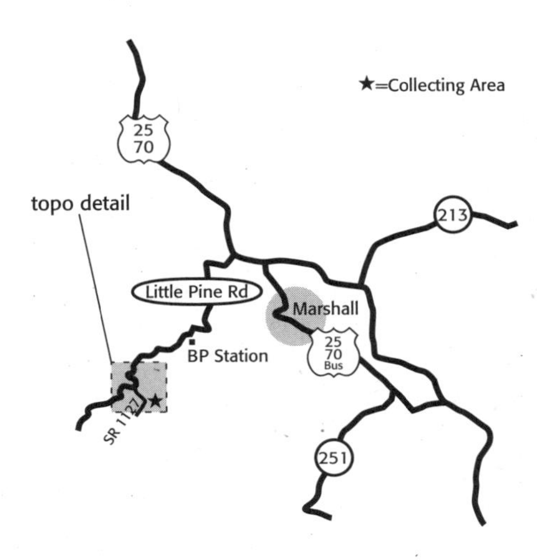

Directions:

From the traffic light at Ingle's grocery store in Marshall, travel 1.5 miles west on Hwy. 25/70 to Little Pine Rd. Turn left on Little Pine Rd. and drive 2.3 miles to the BP Service Station on the south side of the French Broad River, where you must sign in with the cashier and pay $10 per person to collect. From there, continue on Little Pine Rd. 2.6 miles to SR 1127. Turn left and drive 0.4 mile south. Take a 30-degree, left-hand turn onto a gravel driveway (be careful turning; it is on a blind curve). You will cross a small stream at about 300 ft. (don't use the old bridge). Park in the open area to the right after crossing the stream. On foot, proceed north up the dirt road that roughly parallels the creek. You should pass over a chain strung across the road. Walk approximately 1,000 ft., and as the road bends to the east, you will see the mine adit on your right.

Equipment & Tools:

rock pick, mattock, shovel, crack hammer, gad point, flat chisels, prybar, lantern, flashlight with backup and extra batteries

Shut-In Creek Unakite

Rock: unakite

Unakite takes its name from the Unaka Mountains where it was first discovered. These mountains run along the border of northwestern North Carolina and northeastern Tennessee and are part of the Blue Ridge Mountain chain. Unakite is a mottled rock composed primarily of pink feldspar, green epidote, and white quartz, and can be found in scattered pods throughout Madison County. Unakite can be polished to a glassy sheen and is used as an ornamental stone and lapidary rough for cabochons and sculptures.

The unakite at this location may be collected from the riprap between the road and the creek or from the road cut from which the riprap was derived. Remember that the road builders would rightly frown upon anyone removing rock from any riprap that is helping to hold up the road.

Another unakite location is situated approximately 1.1 miles west of Bluff. This site can be reached by driving 0.7 mile northwest on Garenflo Gap Rd. (SR 1173) from Hwy. 209 at Bluff to Bluff Mountain Rd. (SR 1174). Turn left (west) on Bluff Mountain Rd. and drive 0.8 mile to a road cut containing unakite.

Unakite

Latitude & Longitude:

35° -51'-46.83"N
82° -54'-23.81"W

Elevation:

2,511 ft

(from Lemon Gap Quadrangle)

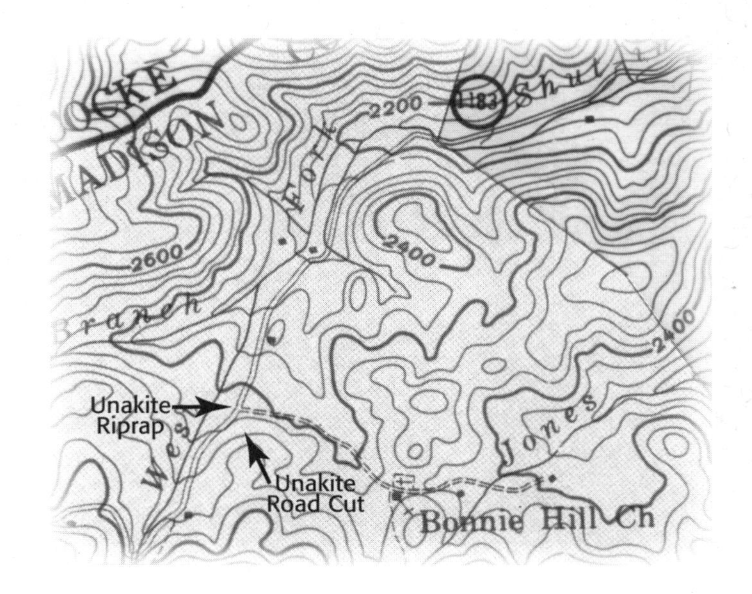

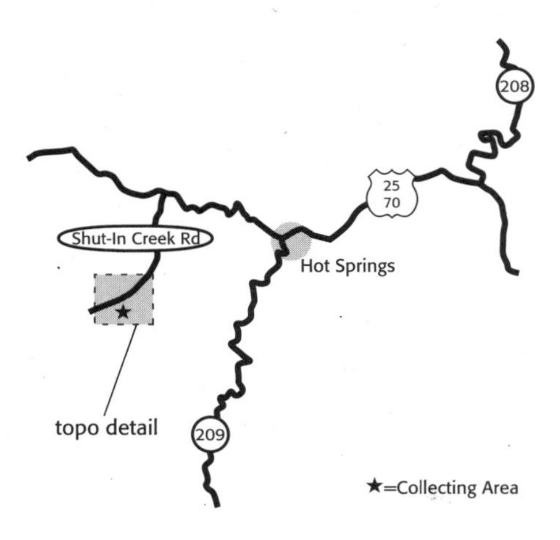

Directions:

From the intersection of Hwy. 209 and Hwy. 25/70 in Hot Springs, drive 3.3 miles west on Hwy. 25/70 and turn left (south) on Shut-In Creek Rd. (SR 1183). Drive 4.3 miles on Shut-In Creek Rd. to a road cut and riprap containing unakite.

Equipment & Tools:

rock pick, crack hammer, and sledgehammer

Stackhouse Mines

Minerals:
barite, fluorite (rare)

Barite was first discovered in the Hot Springs area of Madison County by William Maclure in 1818. Large-scale mining began about 1884 when a grinding mill was erected in Warm Springs, which would later become known as Hot Springs. Barite was mined on and off until about 1927, with most of the production coming from the Stackhouse, Betts, and Gahagan properties between 1904 to 1916 (Stuckey 1965). The Stackhouse area mines are an extensive series of shafts, narrow tunnels, and open pits that run for over half a mile along strike. The subsurface workings were hand dug and blasted as much as 350 ft. below ground surface to follow barite veins (Hunter 1949). The Carolina Barytes Company organized by Henry J. Moore in 1903 processed the barite in a mill that was erected at Stackhouse in 1904. The mill ran on water power supplied by a small wooden dam built across the French Broad River. The dam and mill were destroyed in a 1916 flood and were never replaced (Stuckey 1965).

Three types of barite can found in the Stackhouse area dump piles: 1) fine, grainy, white crystalline barite; 2) coarsely crystalline light to dark gray vitreous barite; and 3) laminated, fine-grained pink barite with disseminated fluorite. Since the mines have not been worked for more than 75 years, the dump piles and mine workings are extremely overgrown with foliage and difficult to locate. The proper use of a map and compass is a must at this location.

Barite

Latitude & Longitude:

35° -52'-17.15"N
82° 45'-18.17"W

Elevation:

1,993 ft

(from Spring Creek Quadrangle)

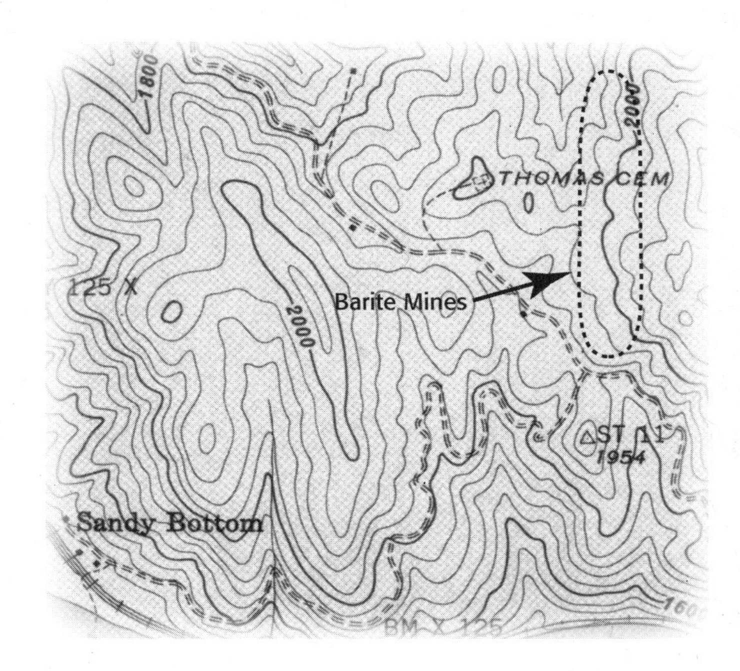

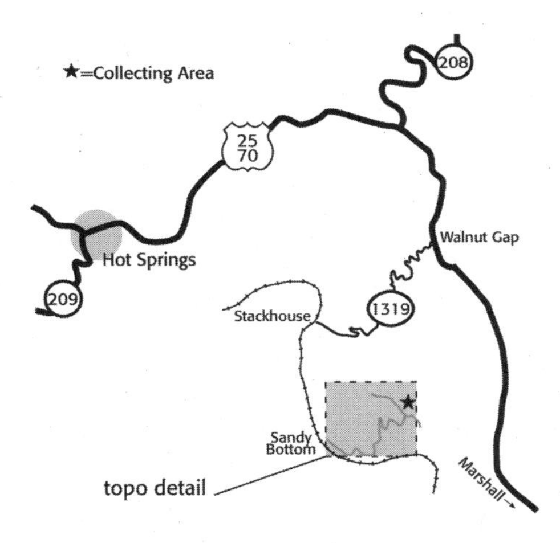

Directions:

From Marshall, drive approximately 9 miles north on Hwy. 25/70 to Walnut Gap. Turn left (west) on SR 1319 and drive 2.7 miles to the end of the road at Stackhouse on the French Broad River and park. Walk about 1.4 miles on the railroad tracks paralleling the river to Sandy Bottom, a small group of summer cottages. Head east just past the last cottage and hike up the slope into the woods until you intersect a doubletrack road. At this point the road heads southeast, but it will twist and turn and eventually head northeast for a total distance of about 1.6 miles, where it ends at a second double-track road running northwest-southeast. The abandoned mine workings are located throughout the forest, trending 10 degrees east of north for approximately 0.5 miles from this intersection.

Equipment & Tools:

rock pick, mattock, scratching tools, crack hammer

McDowell County

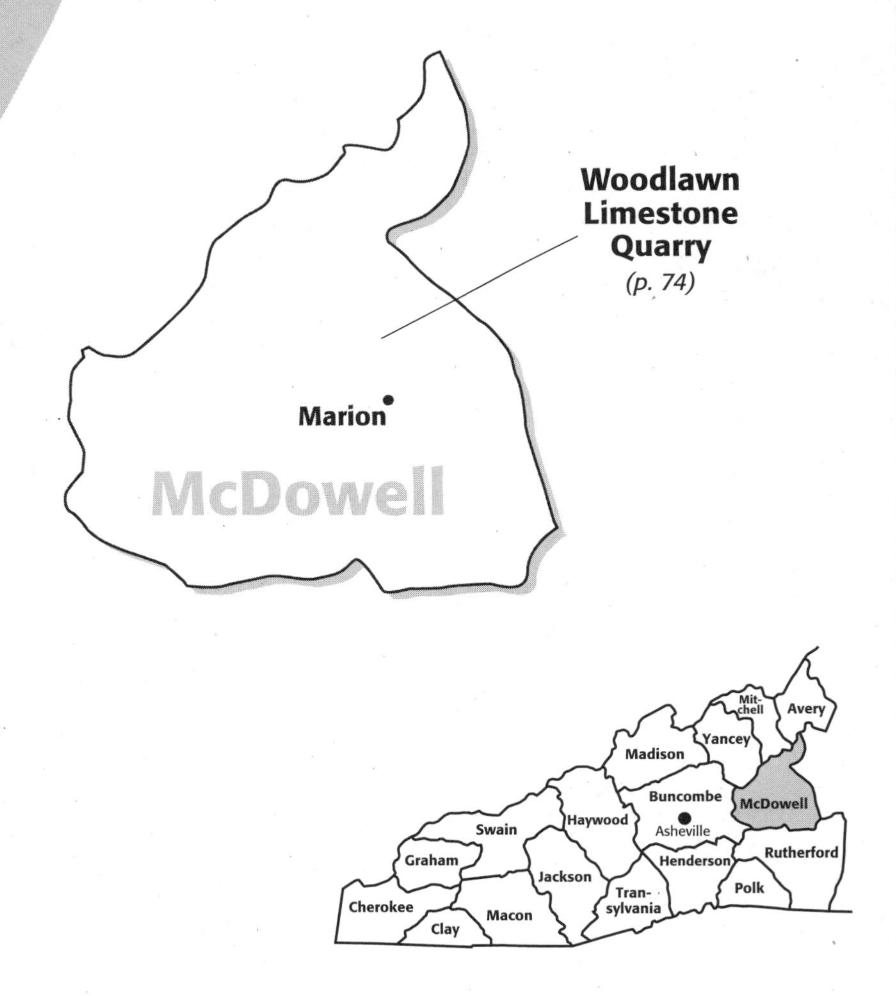
Woodlawn
Limestone
Quarry
(p. 74)
Marion
McDowell
Mit-
chell
Avery
Yancey
Madison
Buncombe
McDowell
Haywood
Asheville
Swain
Rutherford
Henderson
Graham
Jackson
Polk
Tran-
sylvania
Cherokee
Macon
Clay

Woodlawn Limestone Quarry

Minerals:
dog tooth calcite,
small quartz
with phantoms

The dolomitic limestone at the Woodlawn Quarry is a part of the Shady Dolomite formation that outcrops in McDowell County along the valley of the North Fork of the Catawba River. Local residents used the limestone from this site to produce lime in beehive kilns before the War Between the States. In the mid-1930s, the North Carolina State Highway and Public Works Commission opened the Woodlawn Quarry to furnish crushed stone for road construction and agricultural lime (Conrad 1960) and operated it until 1965 (Stuckey 1965). A relatively small, family-owned enterprise called the Explosive Supply Company of Spruce Pine, North Carolina, owns and operates the mine today, mostly for crushed stone.

Quartz plate

Dogtooth calcite crystals up to about 1 in. can be found, although rarely, in sporadic small pockets in the quarry limestone. Individual and plates of milky to water-clear quartz crystals up to 2 in. in diameter and 3 in. long can be collected as float material. The best collection method is to scratch and dig up to 3 ft. below grade into the red-colored soils in the woods about 0.25 mile northeast of the main quarry. This is an active quarry, and you must get permission to enter.

Woodlawn Limestone Quarry

Latitude & Longitude:
35° -46'-56.53"N
82° 02'-02.84"W
(quartz)

Elevation:
1,574 ft

(from Little Switzerland Quadrangle)

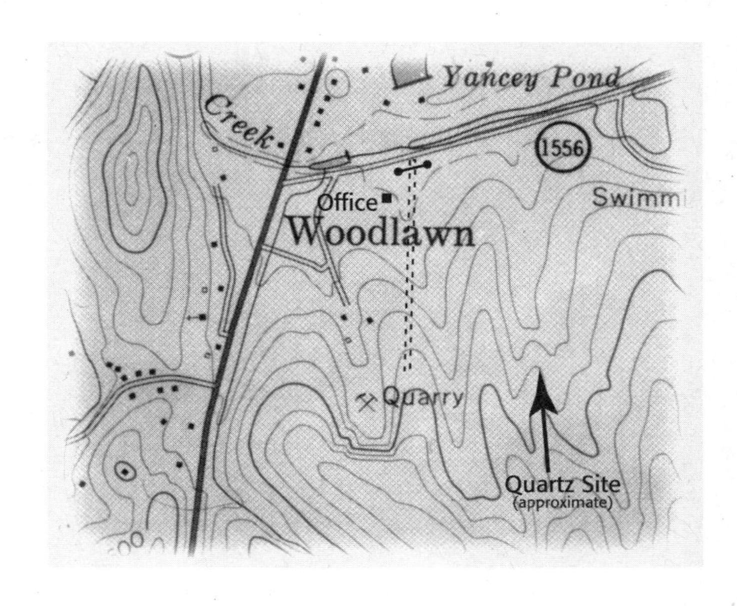

Woodlawn
★=Collecting Area
221
226
topo detail
70
Marion

Directions:

From the intersection of Hwys. 70 and 221/226 in Marion, drive about 6.2 miles north on Hwy. 221/226 to SR 1556 in Woodlawn. Turn right (east) and drive approximately 0.2 mile to the quarry entrance gate. The quarry is located about 0.3 mile due east of the mine office. The quartz-collecting location itself is situated in the forest about 0.5 mile southeast of the office. To get there, drive 300 yd. south and park next to a small open pit to the east of the main road. Walk east along a footpath about 150 yd. to the top of the steep cut bank until you intersect a doubletrack road. Follow the road, taking a near immediate left fork to the east and then southeast as it roughly parallels the slope. Walk for about 0.3 mile until the road turns for the second time from southeast to northeast. Head due south up slope just past a shallow draw for 200 yd., and look for diggings.

Equipment & Tools:

rock pick, crack hammer, chisels, mattock, shovel, scratching tools

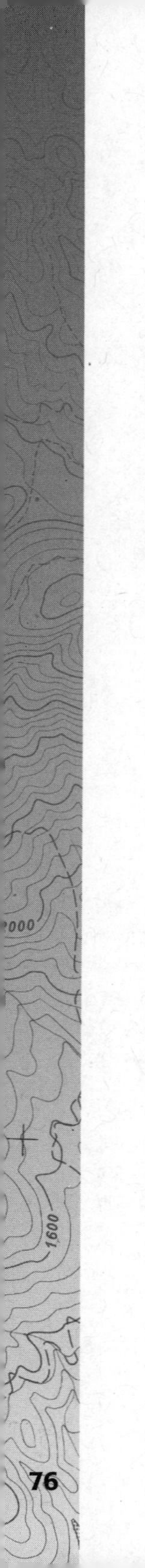
2000
1600

Mitchell County

Entrance to Hootowl Mine near Estatoe

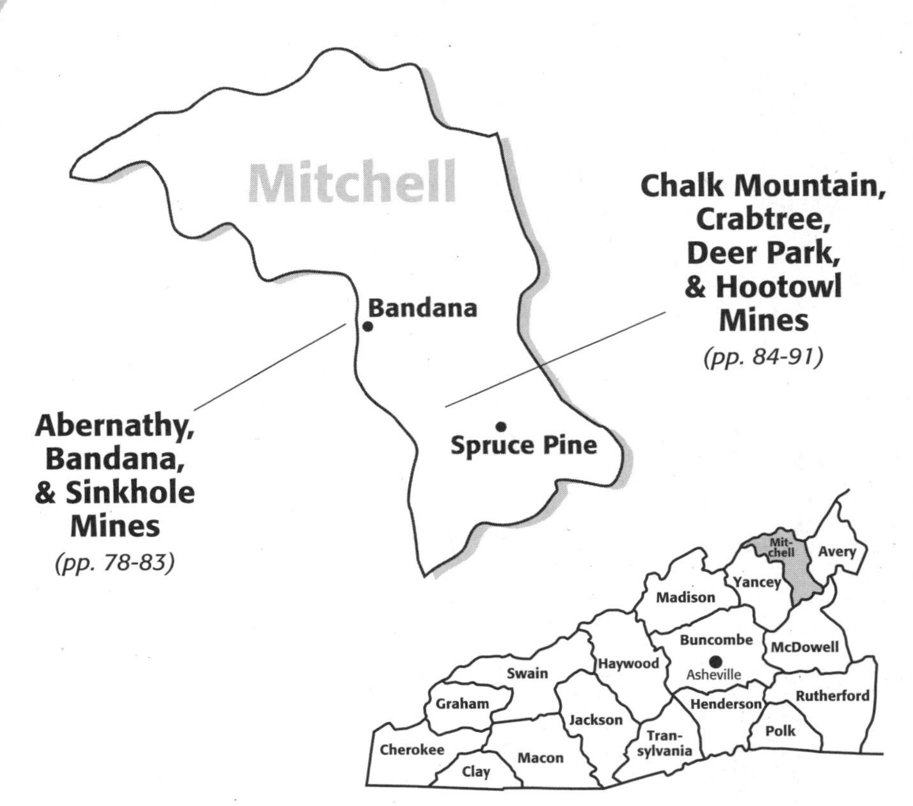

Abernathy Mine

Minerals:
muscovite, garnet, apatite, feldspar

The Abernathy mica mine located in the Bandana area of the Spruce Pine pegmatite district has a long history; large-sheet mica was mined in the years 1880-1903, 1931, 1933, 1938-1940, 1942-1944, and 1953-1962 (Lesure 1968).

The Abernathy mine is arguably the best place in the Spruce Pine district to find apatite; complete bluish-green apatite crystals as large as 1 in. in diameter and 4 in. long have been found. Most of the apatite is partially weathered and somewhat fractured, but complete gemmy crystals can occasionally be found. Gemmy almandine garnet crystals reportedly as large as 2 in. can also be found. Sort through the tailings at the river's edge for minerals. You can also collect in the upper spoil piles, accessible by climbing the steep slope that rises abruptly to the east of the tracks. Extensive mine tailings, cuts, and drifts are located in the forest several hundred yards east and north of the main adit. An air-venting tunnel for the underground mine workings was cut at railroad level about 100 yd. south of the riverside mine tailings.

Above: Apatite crystal in mica
Below: Apatite crystal in pegmatite

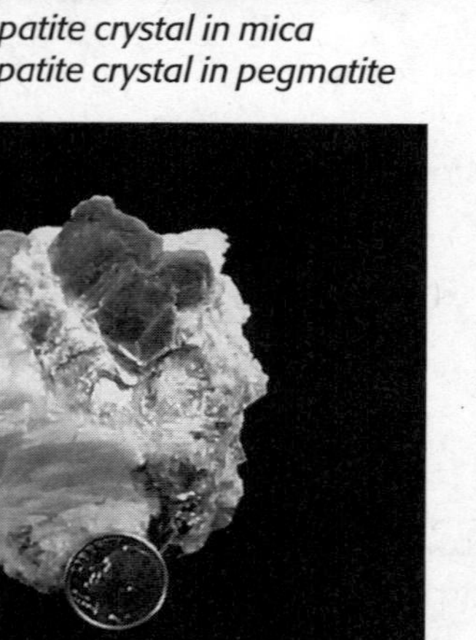

Latitude & Longitude:

35° -58'-13.72"N
82° -11'-24.93"W

Elevation:

2,470 ft

(from Micaville Quadrangle)

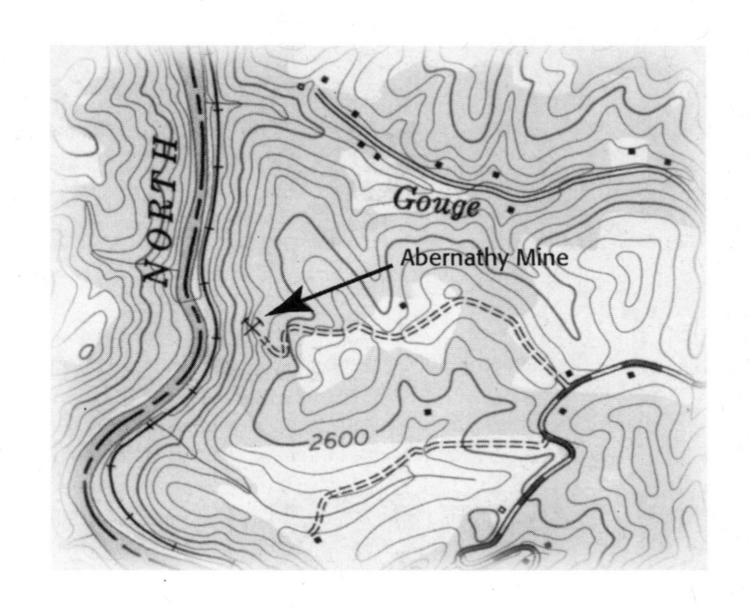

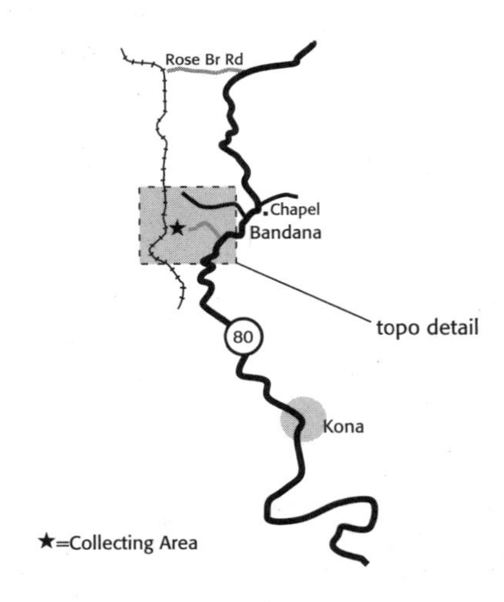

Directions:

Drive approximately 2 miles north on Hwy. 80 from Silver Chapel Church in Bandana to Rose Branch Rd. Turn left (west) and drive 0.9 mile to the end of the road at the railroad tracks. Walk about 1.5 miles south on railroad tracks until you see pegmatite spoil piles below the tracks next to the river. The mine is located about 200 ft. east of the railroad tracks. Watch carefully for trains, as this stretch of railroad is still quite active.

Equipment & Tools:

rock pick, mattock, crack hammer, gad point, flat chisels

Bandana Dolomitic Marble

Minerals:
white marble, kyanite, wollastonite

The Bandana dolomitic marble is the only known occurrence of carbonate rock in Mitchell County. Limestone that would eventually become the Bandana dolomitic marble was most likely deposited as many as 500 million years ago in a shallow sea on what was then the eastern edge of the continental shelf. During or after its formation, the limestone (calcium carbonate) came into contact with magnesium-rich water and was altered to dolostone (calcium-magnesium carbonate) when some of its calcium was replaced with magnesium. The dolostone became buried deep within the earth's surface, and heat and pressure caused the rock to crystallize into a metamorphic rock called dolomitic marble.

Wollastonite on marble

This deposit is composed of white, uniformly coarse-grained dolomitic marble cut by an irregular pegmatite. Although it has been estimated that the deposit contains nearly 500,000 tons of high-grade dolomitic marble and is favorably situated for quarrying, it has never been mined (Conrad 1960). Small blue kyanite and white wollastonite crystals can also be found at this location.

White dolomitic marble

Latitude & Longitude:
35° -58'-53.62"N
82° -11'-26.00"W

Elevation:
2,312 ft

(from Micaville Quadrangle)

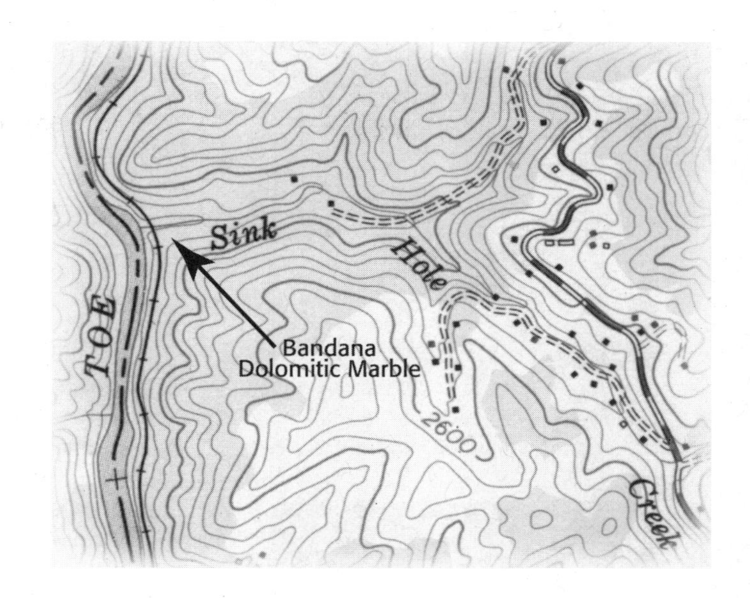

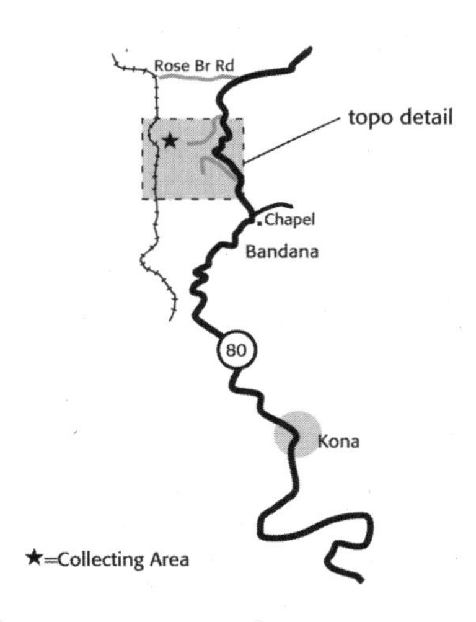

Directions:

Drive approximately 2 miles north on Hwy. 80 from Silver Chapel Church in Bandana to Rose Branch Rd. Turn left (west) and drive 0.9 mile to the end of the road at the railroad tracks. Walk about 0.66 miles south on the railroad tracks to Sinkhole Creek. Follow a small trail to the left (east) just south of the creek, and walk about 100 yd. to a marble outcrop. Watch carefully for trains on the tracks, as this stretch of the railroad is still quite active.

Equipment & Tools:

rock pick, crack hammer, gad point, flat chisels

Sinkhole Mine

Minerals:
muscovite, garnet, apatite, kyanite, feldspar

Sinkhole Mine is considered to be one of the 10 or 12 oldest mica mines in the country. U. S. Congressman, Senator, and Confederate officer Thomas L. Clingman was drawn to the area in 1867 upon rumors of ancient Spanish silver mines. Clingman, who studied mineralogy under Professor Elisha Mitchell, a Connecticut Yankee who was immortalized by having the highest mountain east of the Mississippi named for him, discovered a series of long-abandoned pits dug into hillsides opposite Sinkhole Creek. Stone tools left behind by ancient Native American miners were found in the pits. Mica from North Carolina was used extensively in ceremonial and burial mounds erected by Native American tribes in the Ohio Valley up to 2,000 years ago; mica images were discovered there, including stylized human torsos, hands, claws and talons, and geometric figures. One mound at Hopewell Cultural National Historic Park near Chillicothe, Ohio, is called "the mica grave" because one of the 13 graves within it is lined with rectangular sheets of mica up to 10 by 14 in. (Margolin 1999).

Above: Feldspar
Below: Apatite in pegmatite

Clingman sank a shaft in 1868 to begin the modern era of mica mining at Sinkhole Mine. His hopes to find silver were dashed, but he did find mica sheets as large as he had ever seen. Mining at the Sinkhole Mine continued for about 94 years at intervals that reflected the selling price of mica. Numerous shafts, adits, drifts, and cuts were dug in the years 1868-1879, 1906-1910, 1914-1920, 1940-1945, and 1952-1962 (Lesure 1968).

The minerals listed above can be found by scratching in the extensive spoil piles or by breaking apart larger rocks. Shortwave ultraviolet light is a useful tool after dark to find apatite crystals that fluoresce bright yellow.

Latitude & Longitude:
35° -58'-32.24"N
82° -10'-35.42"W

Elevation:
2,650 ft

(from Micaville Quadrangle)

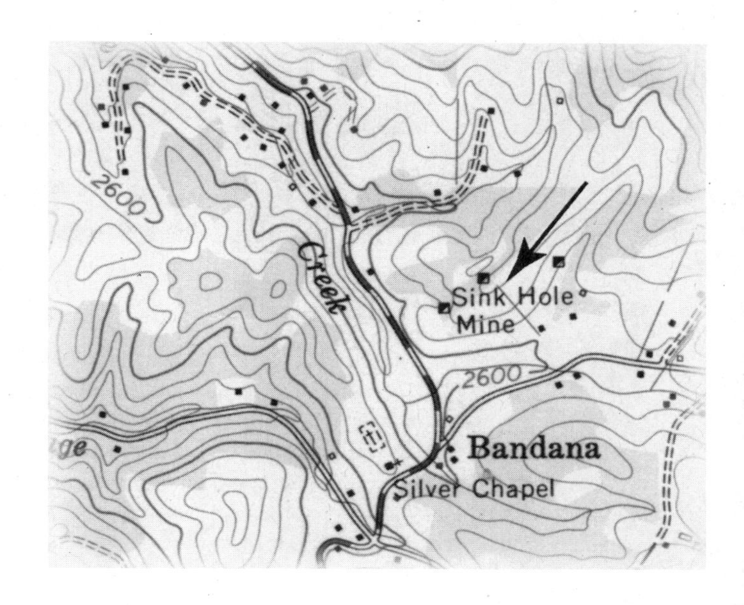

topo detail
Chapel
Bandana
80
Kona
★=Collecting Area

Directions:
Drive approximately 0.25 mile north on Hwy. 80 from Silver Chapel Church in Bandana. The mine is about 100 yd. east of Hwy 80.

Equipment & Tools:
rock pick, mattock, crack hammer, gad point, flat chisels, scratching tools

Sinkhole Mine

Chalk Mountain Mine

Minerals:
torbernite, hyalite opal, autunite, feldspar

The Chalk Mountain Mine was worked for mica in the early 1900s, in 1930, and during World War II (Lesure 1968). The mine is currently operated for feldspar and quartz by the Feldspar Corporation.

Access to the mine is strictly prohibited except for at least one nighttime guided collecting trip for fluorescent minerals, offered in conjunction with the annual rock and mineral show in Spruce Pine in late July or early August. The minerals come alive in the dark under shortwave ultraviolet light; the hyalite opal and some of the feldspar fluoresce bright green and red, respectively. Chalk Mountain hyalite opal is said to be the most highly fluorescent in the world. Torbernite and autunite may also be found associated with the hyalite opal. Call the Mitchell County Chamber of Commerce in Spruce Pine, North Carolina at 800-227-3915 or 828-765-9483 to reserve a spot on the annual collecting trip.

Hyalite opal on quartz and feldspar

Torbernite on quartz (less than 4mm)

Latitude & Longitude:

35° -54'-05.13"N
82° -06'-05.94"W

Elevation:

3,161 ft

(from Spruce Pine Quadrangle)

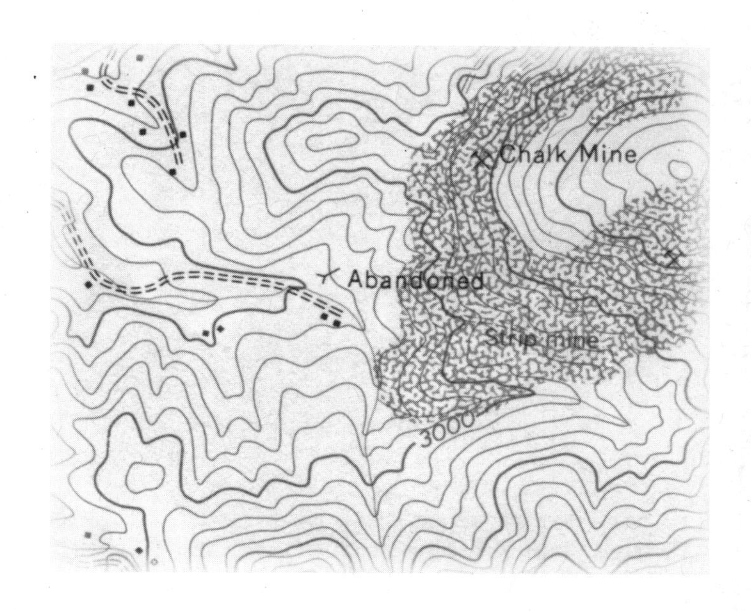

Directions:

Access to the mine is strictly prohibited except for at least one nighttime guided collecting trip for fluorescent minerals, offered in conjunction with the annual rock and mineral show in Spruce Pine in late July or early August. Call the Mitchell County Chamber of Commerce in Spruce Pine at 800-227-3915 or 828-765-9483 to reserve a spot on the annual collecting trip.

Equipment & Tools:

rock pick, crack hammer, gad point, flat chisels, short wave ultraviolet light

View from Chalk Mountain

Crabtree Emerald Mine

Minerals:
emerald, golden beryl, aquamarine, tourmaline, smoky quartz, garnet, feldspar

Emerald was discovered in July 1894 by J. L. Rorison and D. A. Bowman in a pegmatite dike on the east flank of Crabtree Mountain. Perfect hexagonal, facet-grade emeralds as large as 1.1 in. by 2 in. were recovered, but most were much smaller in size (Stuckey 1965). An inclined shaft was cut to follow the pegmatite dike, but it was worked only sporadically. The most recent mining concentrated on recovering small emeralds in matrix, which is a sought-after lapidary and display material. Today, a small pond covering the shaft sits in the center of the spoil piles. The minerals listed above can be found by breaking apart larger rocks or screening the spoil piles that surround the pond.

Crabtree Emerald Mine

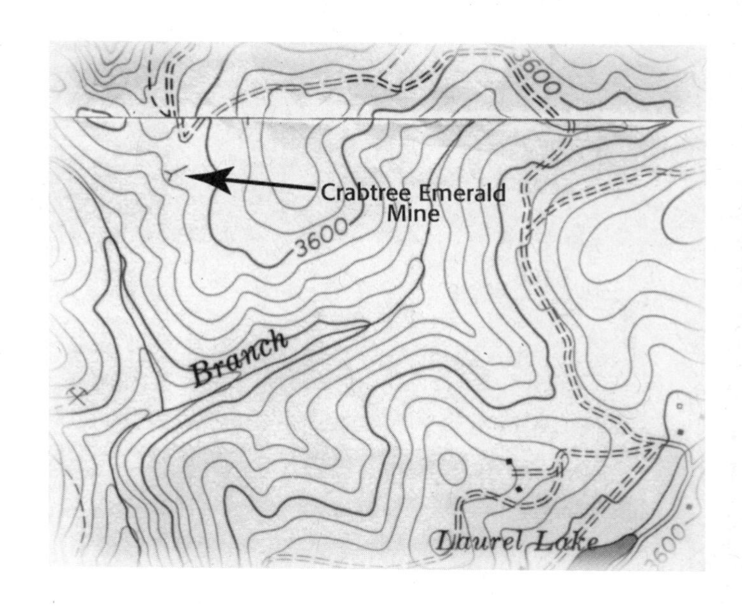

Latitude & Longitude:

35° -52′-25.94″N
82° -07′-14.25″W

Elevation:

3,543 ft

(from Spruce Pine and Little Switzerland Quadrangles)

1105
Laurel Lake
topo detail
1104
Chestnut Grove Church
1100
Blue Ridge Pkwy
Little Switzerland
226A
★=Collecting Area

Directions:

Starting at the intersection of the Blue Ridge Parkway and SR 1100 at Little Switzerland, drive 1.1 miles north-northwest on SR 1100 to Chestnut Grove Church, built with black and white amphibolite rock. Circle east and then north around the church and go northwest on SR 1104. Continue 1.1 miles north on SR 1104 past Laurel Lake on the left, and turn left (northwest) on SR 1105. Take the right fork at 0.1 mile and the left fork at 0.5 mile, continuing on SR 1105 for a total of 1.3 miles to mine workings just to the south of the road.

Emerald in matrix

Equipment & Tools:

rock pick, mattock, shovel,
crack hammer, gad point, flat chisels,
quarter-inch mesh screen

Deer Park Mine

Minerals:
feldspar, garnet, muscovite, thulite, hyalite, smoky quartz, garnet, monazite

The Deer Park Mine was worked for mica and feldspar from 1911-1939, from 1942-1945, and again in 1954 (Lesure 1968). A series of shafts, cuts, drifts and adits dot the area. The minerals listed above can be found by scratching in the spoil piles located along the river and on the forested slopes above them. As of this writing, a housing development is being constructed in the area that encompasses the Deer Park Mine, bringing an end to collecting at this specific location. However, the spoil piles from the Deer Park and other nearby mica and pegmatite mines will likely remain accessible on both sides of the North Toe River, especially on the north bank. The latitude, longitude, elevation, and directions for this collecting site pertain to a small pegmatite outcrop on the north side of the river where the garnet in mica (muscovite) specimen pictured at left was collected (see map).

Garnet in mica

Muscovite

Latitude & Longitude:

35° -56'-02.71"N
82° -06'-19.95"W

Elevation:

2,475 ft

(from Spruce Pine Quadrangle)

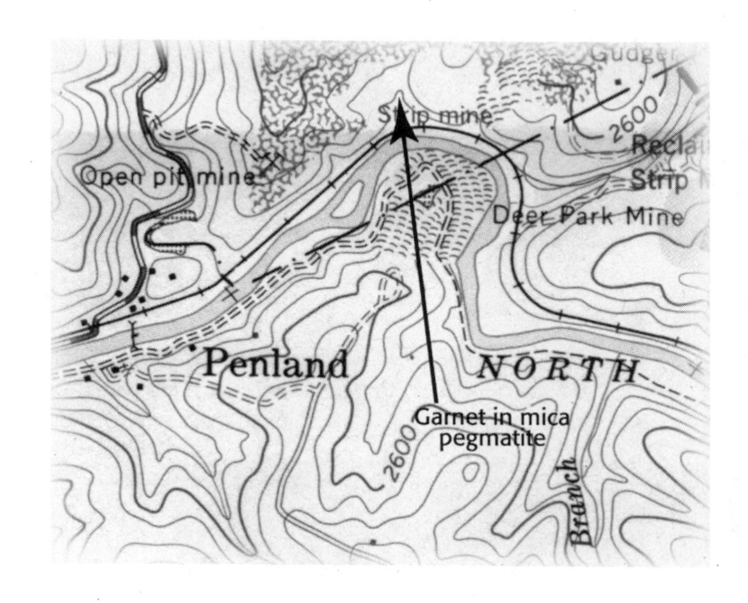

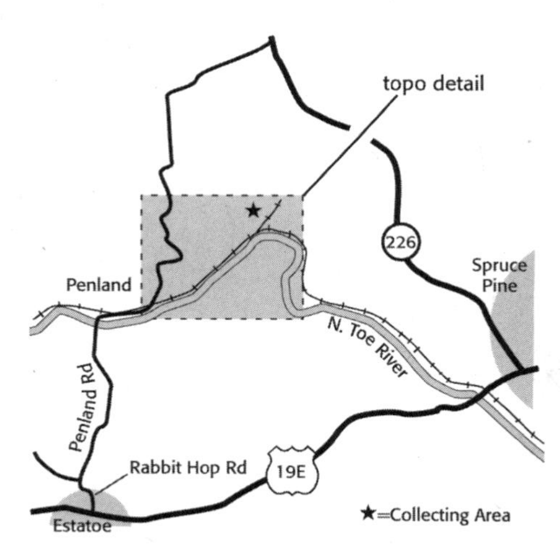

Directions:

From Estatoe, located about 3 miles west of Spruce Pine on Hwy. 19E, drive 0.2 mile north on Rabbit Hop Rd. (SR 1160) to Penland Rd. (SR 1162). Turn right (north) and drive 2.3 miles to the Penland Post Office on the right, about 300 yd. after crossing the bridge over the North Toe River. Park out of the way in the parking lot. Proceed on foot, walking northeast on the railroad tracks for about 0.5 miles. Keep an eye out for trains, as these are active tracks. When you come to a fork in the tracks, take the left fork. The pegmatite outcrop containing garnet in mica is located about 100 yd. past the railroad junction above the left side of the abandoned stretch of tracks.

Equipment & Tools:

rock pick, mattock, crack hammer,
gad point, flat chisels, scratching tools

Hootowl Mine

Minerals:
muscovite, albite, orthoclase, smoky quartz, garnet

The Hootowl mine was worked for large sheet mica and feldspar from 1937 to 1939 and sporadically thereafter until the early 1960s (Lesure 1968). The mine walls rise over 150 ft. to a ceiling that looms over a dusty, rock-strewn floor and clear pool of water. The inside of this mine offers a wonderful glimpse into the interior of a large pegmatite containing large sheets of muscovite and amphibolite xenoliths. The minerals listed above can be found by scratching in the extensive soil piles located outside the mine.

Muscovite, feldspar, and quartz pegmatite

Hootowl Mine in autumn

Latitude & Longitude:

35° -53′-01.24″N
82° -07′-45.85″W

Elevation:

3,263 ft

(from Micaville and Spruce Pine Quadrangles)

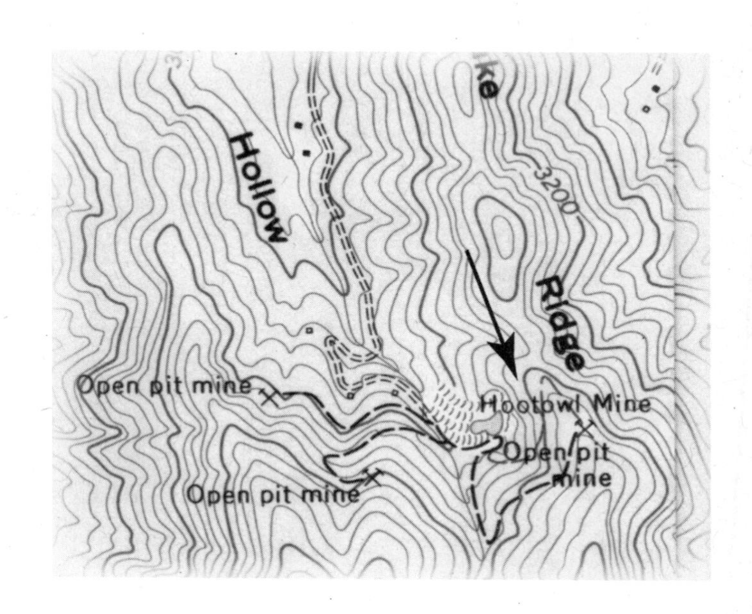

★=Collecting Area
Penland
226
Spruce Pine
80
19E
Estatoe
Hootowl Rd.
topo detail

Directions:

From Estatoe, located about 3 miles west of Spruce Pine on 19E, drive 0.5 mile south on Hootowl Rd. (SR 1157). Turn right (west) at 0.5 mile to stay on Hootowl Rd. Continue driving for another 0.8 mile to a gate. Park on the side of the road near the gate (don't block the road or gate). If you are greeted by four or five friendly hound dogs, you are in the right place. Walk on the gravel road about 0.4 mile and turn left onto a side road that goes east up an incline. Walk an additional 0.4 mile bearing right (south) after the first 100 yd. and then left (east) after the next 300 yd. Follow the small stream in the road past the large pond to the mine.

Equipment & Tools:

rock pick, mattock, crack hammer, gad point, flat chisels, scratching tools

Swain County

Nantahala Talc & Limestone Quarry, offering an excellent view of the beautiful Nantahala Gorge.

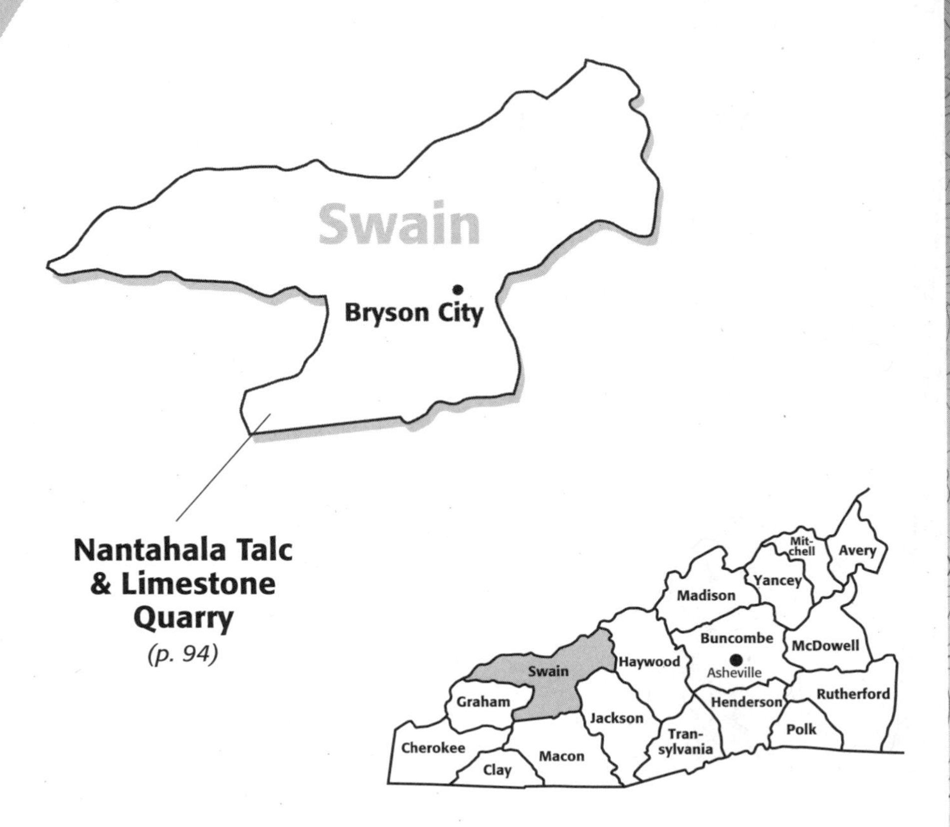

Nantahala Talc & Limestone Quarry

Rocks & Minerals:
banded marble, calcite, talc, travertine, tremolite, pyrite, quartz, aragonite, speleothems

The Nantahala Talc & Limestone Quarry is located in the beautiful Nantahala Gorge, home to the Nantahala River, one of the finest whitewater rafting rivers in the country.

Except for a short period during World War I, the Nantahala Quarry has been in continuous operation since it was opened in 1890 by the North Carolina Mining & Talc Company. The Nantahala Talc and Limestone Company began large-scale development of the quarry in1938 and1939 and continues to own and operate the mine to this day. Crushed stone is the principle product, but agricultural lime, terrazzo chips, and ground talc for crayons have also been produced in the past (Conrad 1960).

The most striking material in the mine is a banded and mottled rock composed of variable layers of pink, black, gray, and tan marble. Most of the marble is badly fractured and schistose, with thin layers of serpentine coating schistosity planes. This marble and the other minerals listed above can be found by scratching through the spoil piles or by breaking apart larger rocks. This is an active mine; you must get permission to enter.

Above: Banded marble
Below: Travertine dripstone

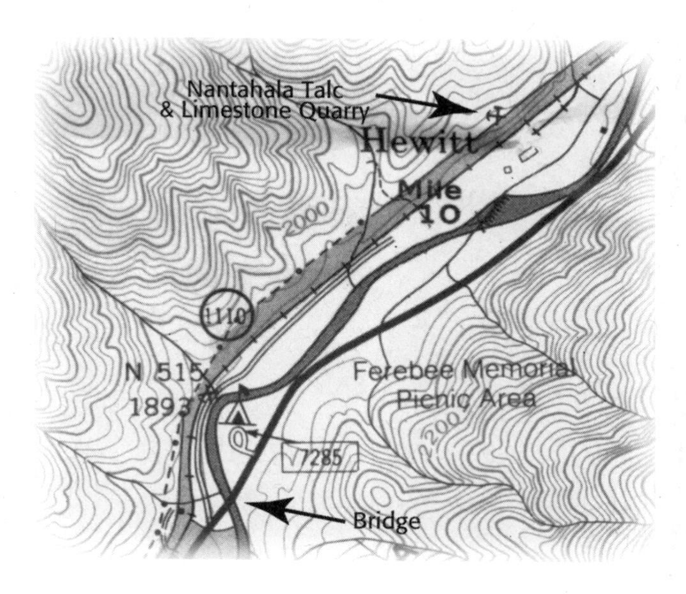

Latitude & Longitude:

35° -18′-33.97″N
83° -38′-51.58″W

Elevation:

1,971 ft

(from Hewitt Quadrangle)

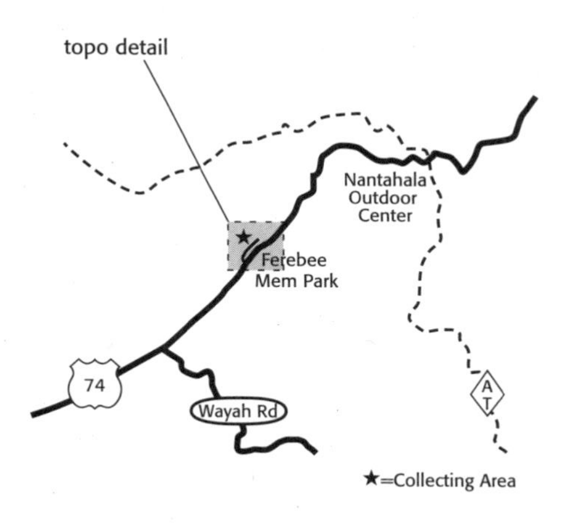

Directions:

From Nantahala Outdoor Center on Hwy. 74, drive 5.7 miles southwest along the south banks of the Nantahala River. Turn right (north) on a gravel road just after crossing a bridge over the river. Drive approximately 0.6 mile to the quarry gate and office.

Equipment & Tools:

rock pick, mattock, crack hammer, gad point, flat chisels, prybar

2000
1600

Transylvania County

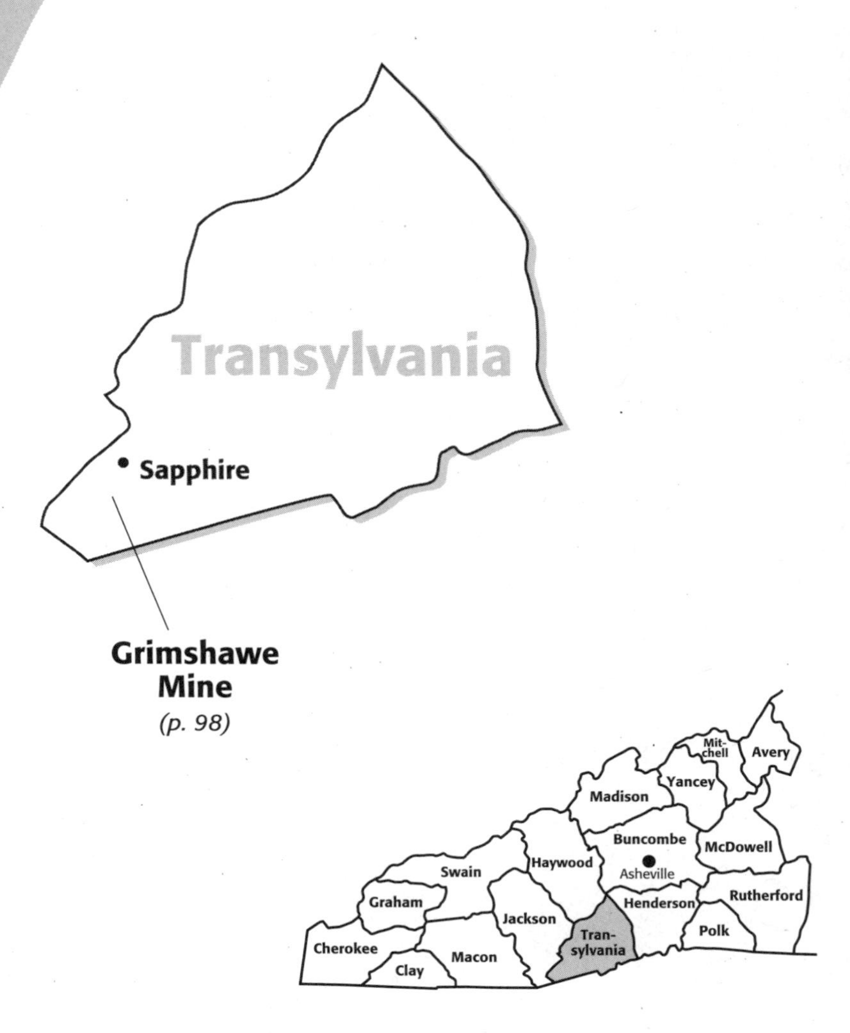

Grimshawe Mine

Minerals:
sapphire, ruby, corundum

Much of the history of the Grimshawe Mine is unclear. Even the name Grimshawe Mine is questionable, and exactly when commercial mining took place at this location is difficult to determine. However, it is known that the mine was worked for asbestos in peridotite, and this mining most likely occurred between 1930 and 1950 (Stuckey 1965). Former mine workers report that sapphires and rubies were often seen while working the mine. The exact source of the corundum is not known, but it may be derived from local granite pegmatites. A small pegmatite mine is located approximately 0.5 mile north of this location.

To find facet-grade ruby and sapphire, you will need to dig a hole near the creek deep enough to intersect a gravel layer at around 3 ft. to 6 ft. below grade, then use a quarter-inch screen to sort the material in the creek. Some collectors choose to dig right next to the creek. Others opt to dig farther away in the forest, which requires hauling heavy buckets of gravely soils to the creek for screening.

Above: Sapphire and ruby
Below: Grimshawe Mine

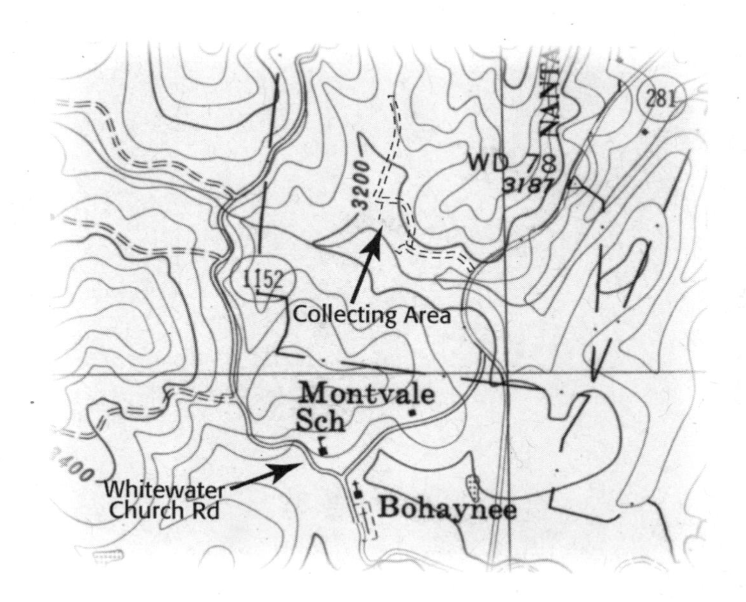

Latitude & Longitude:

35° -04'-06.28"N
83° -00'-34.59"W

Elevation:

3,191 ft

(from Cashiers Quadrangle)

to Cashiers
64
Sapphire
Whitewater Ch Rd
281
topo detail
★=Collecting Area

Directions:

From Hwy. 64 approximately 3 miles east of the village of Sapphire, drive approximately 5.4 miles south on Hwy. 281 to a Forest Service road on the right. Turn right (west) on the Forest Service road, drive approximately 200 yd. and park, proceeding from this point on foot. Take an immediate right fork up a slight incline and follow the doubletrack Forest Service road west for approximately 0.25 mile until you reach an outcropping of asbestos-bearing peridotite. Go south along a footpath leading into the woods and locate the rock-collecting holes and material to be screened along the creek.

Equipment & Tools:

rock pick, mattock, shovel, scratching tools, quarter-inch mesh screen

2000
1600

Yancey County

Spoil piles outside the Ray Mine, south of Burnsville

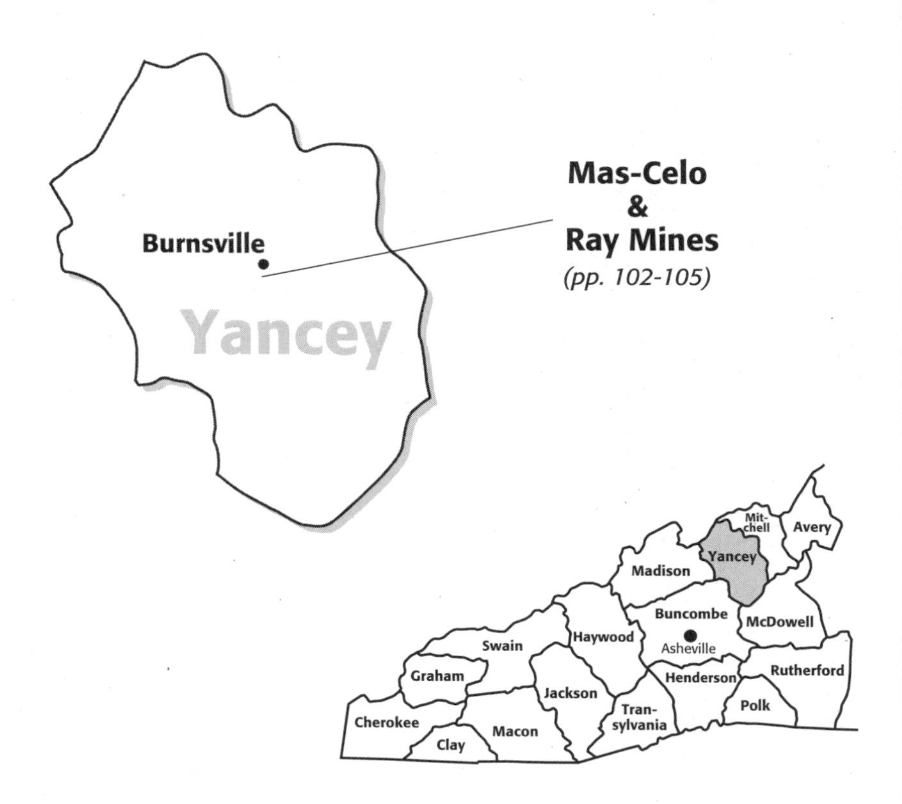

Mas-Celo Kyanite Mine

Minerals:
kyanite, garnet

Kyanite was mined at this location from 1931 to 1941 by Celo Mines, Inc., which obtained a 99-year lease on the property from the Yancey Kyanite Company in 1930. In 1941, the mine changed ownership from Celo Mines, Inc., to Mas-Celo Mines, Inc., which continued operating it until June 1942. Kyanite was extracted mostly from open pits, although an adit was driven into the side of the mountain for about 150 ft. The Yancey Kyanite Company endeavored to continue mining operations with equipment owned by the Metals Reserve Company from April 1, 1943, until June 1, 1943. Although in April of 1943 the Yancey Kyanite Company became a contracted agent for the Metals Reserve Company for a period of five years, mining operations were never started up again (U. S. Department of the Interior 1943).

Kyanite-bearing rocks can be found in the spoil piles and sometimes along the roads leading up to the mine workings. The kyanite specimen shown on the facing page was found on the doubletrack road leading up to the mine workings. The spoil piles are located in the forest, down gradient of the adit, and inside the two major open pits which are 100 yd. or so southeast of the adit. Rocks containing sky-blue kyanite blades up to 5 in. long and 2 in. wide have been found at this location.

Entrance to the Mas-Celo adit in summer

Latitude & Longitude:
35° -53′-34.72″N
82° -16′-01.27″W

Elevation:
3,839 ft

(from Burnsville Quadrangle)

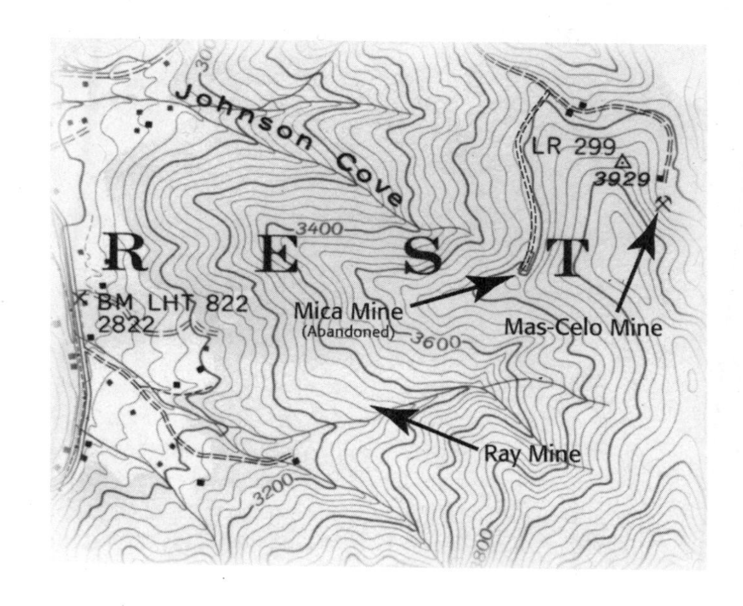

197
19E
Burnsville
Bowlens Cr Rd
topo detail
Bowlens Creek Church
SR 1192
197
★=Collecting Area

Directions:
From the Ray Mine (see directions, p. 105), hike approximately 0.5 mile at a bearing of 45 degrees to an abandoned mica mine. You will find an old road at the north end of the mine cut. Walk north on this road for about 0.3 mile to an intersection with a second road. Go right (east) and walk about 0.3 mile, passing some old building foundations, to the adit on the south side of the road. Two open pits are located just to the east of the adit.

Equipment & Tools:
rock pick, mattock, crack hammer, gad point, flat chisels

Kyanite

Ray (Wray) Mine

Minerals:
muscovite, aquamarine, albite, plagioclase feldspar (some clear oligoclase), white microcline, columbite, apatite, golden beryl, schorl, fluorite, amazonite

The Ray Mica Mine is a series of cuts, shafts, and stopes that extend in granite pegmatite approximately 650 ft. along a northwest to southeast strike. The mine was first worked for mica in 1869 by Garrett Ray. The mine was closed and reopened many times throughout the years that followed, until the Wray mining company abandoned it as unprofitable in May1944 (Lesure 1968). The Ray mine is arguably the best place in North Carolina to find facetable grade aquamarine, in addition to the other fine minerals listed above. The largest beryl crystals are reported to be about 2 in. in diameter and 4 to 5 in. long, although crystals of this size, especially facetable ones, are rare. The cuts, shafts, and stopes are not accessible and should be avoided. All collecting must be done in the extensive spoil piles extending along a steep slope and beyond the creek that flows through the area. To find minerals, dig up and screen spoil pile materials in the creek, or simply dig into the slope while keeping a sharp eye out for minerals as you do so. Many collectors find crystals by breaking larger rocks. Mica, feldspar, small black tourmaline, and garnet are plentiful, but other accessory minerals are more difficult to find.

Aquamarine crystals

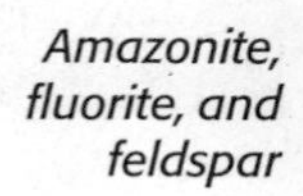

Amazonite, fluorite, and feldspar

Latitude & Longitude:
35° 53′-17.69″N
82° -16′-31.53″W

Elevation:
3,400 ft

(from Burnsville Quadrangle)

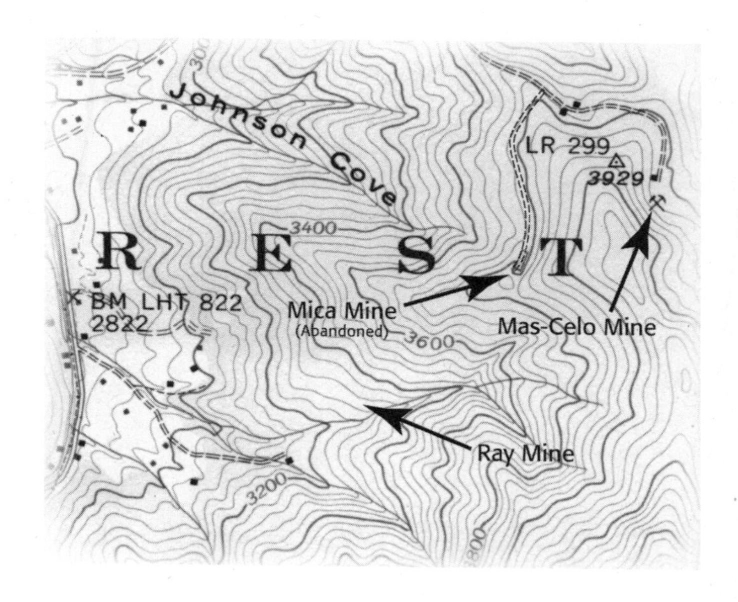

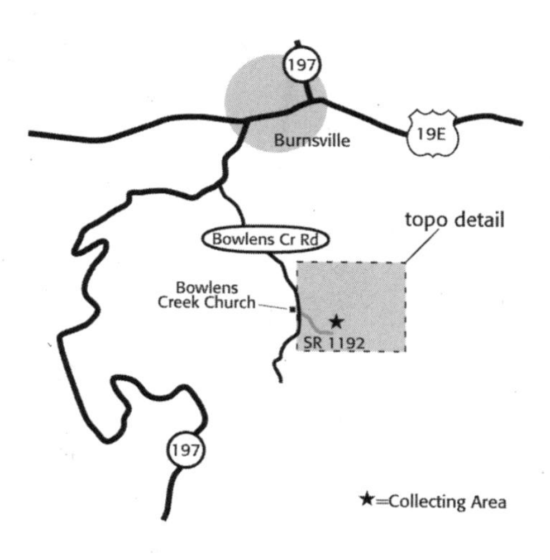

Directions:
From Hwy. 19E in Burnsville, drive 0.9 mile south on Hwy. 197 to Bowlens Creek Rd. Turn left (east) on Bowlens Creek Road and continue 1.5 miles. Turn left onto SR 1192 just past the Bowlens Creek Church. The gravel road becomes unimproved after 0.3 mile, so vehicles unsuited for rough terrain should be parked along the side of the road, and collectors should hike the remaining 0.5 mile to the collecting area. After crossing a small creek, hike or drive up the rocky road that follows the larger creek. Look for diggings and spoil piles along the steep slopes, mostly to the west of the creek.

Equipment & Tools:
rock pick, mattock, shovel, crack hammer, gad point, flat chisels, scratching tools, quarter-inch mesh screen

Appendix

Glossary
Resources
Rock & Mineral Museums
Selected Rock & Mineral Clubs
Gem Mines
References
Index of Minerals & Collecting Sites

Glossary

adit–a nearly horizontal passage from the surface by which a mine is entered.

alluvial–pertaining to materials deposited by stream action.

blade/bladed–a mineral that is generally shaped like the blade of a knife or a fan.

body–a mass of one type of rock sandwiched between another type of rock.

botryoidal–a mineral form that is globular or resembling a bunch of grapes.

cabochon–a highly polished, convex-cut, unfaceted gem.

carbonates–three groups of minerals found mostly in limestone and dolostone: aragonite, calcite, and dolomite.

Catalan forge–a type of forge or furnace for producing wrought iron directly from the ore.

chalcedony–a mineral composed of fibrous microcrystalline quartz.

color zoned–refers to a single crystal that displays different colors due to changes in chemical makeup. Most zoning is concentric and runs parallel to the crystal outline.

cut–an elongated excavation into the ground surface.

detritus–loose disintegrated matter such as fragments that have eroded from rocks and other organic forest materials.

Democrat district–area surrounding the village of Democrat, Buncombe County, North Carolina.

dike–A long mass of igneous rock intruding or cutting across the structure of another rock type.

draw–a gully that is shallower than a ravine.

drift–meaning a horizontal passage dug or blasted underground to follow a mineral or rock vein.

dunite–a dense green colored igneous rock that consists mainly of olivine.

facet grade –gems that are translucent to transparent and can be faceted into cut stones for jewelry.

fault–a slip-surface between two portions of the earth's surface that have moved in different directions relative to each other.

float material–rocks and minerals which have become detached from the bedrock surface and have moved downslope from their points of origin.

gemmy–translucent to transparent materials.

hexagonal—composed of six equal sides.

igneous rock—a rock that has crystallized from a molten state.

intermittent stream—a stream that contains water and flows only during wet periods.

intruded / intrusion—pertaining to igneous rocks or features formed by the emplacement of magma in pre-existing rock.

lense—a layer of one type of rock sandwiched between another type of rock.

magma—molten rock found beneath the earth's surface.

matrix—the whole rock in which a mineral has formed and is contained.

massive—a rock or mineral which, to the naked eye, has no discernable crystalline structure.

metamorphic rock—a rock changed from its original form and/or composition by heat, pressure, and/or chemically active fluids.

opaque—impenetrable by light; neither transparent or translucent.

oxalic acid—a poisonous, colorless, crystalline organic acid found in many plants (such as spinach), and used as a bleach and rust remover.

pegmatite—an extremely coarse-grained igneous rock with interlocking crystals and, usually, a bulk chemical composition similar to granite. Pegmatites are prime sources for many gem-quality precious and semiprecious stones.

peridotite—any of a group of igneous rocks composed mainly of olivine and various pyroxenes, and having a granite-like texture.

plate—a relatively flat and often thin piece of rock that has crystallized minerals on its surface.

pseudomorph—a mineral that has the identical crystalline structure of another mineral but has a different chemical composition. Occurs when the chemical composition of a mineral is replaced with the chemical composition of another mineral while retaining the original crystalline structure (see ***replacement***).

replacement—process by which the chemical composition of a mineral is changed to (replaced with) the chemical composition of another mineral.

riprap—broken stones used for a road or bank foundation.

schistose—parallel alignment of mineral grains in a rock.

Glossary (continued)

sedimentary rock—rock formed from the accumulation of sediment. The sediment may consist of fragments and mineral grains of varying sizes from pre-existing rocks, the remains or products of animals and plants, and/or the products of chemical action.

shaft—a primary vertical or non-vertical opening through mine strata that connects the surface with underground workings.

silk—impurities found in corundum thought to cause the mineral to display a star when properly cut and polished.

sluice box—an artificial, above-ground channel constructed of wood to conduct water for screening soils. Used to separate and recover precious gems and minerals.

stope—an excavation in the form of steps made by the mining of ore from steeply inclined or vertical veins.

spoil piles—see tailings.

strike—the compass direction of the intersection between a structural surface (e.g., a bedding plane of a rock or a fault surface) and the horizontal.

subaerial—located or occurring on or near the surface of the earth.

surface collecting—collecting rock and minerals scattered on the ground surface as opposed to digging into the ground.

tailings—left over and generally unwanted rock debris generated from mining operations.

thrust fault—a type of reverse fault where the fault plane is 15 degrees or less (see *fault*).

troctolite—a type of rock that is composed of olivine with varying amounts of calcic plagioclase feldspar with secondary enstatite, amphibolite, chlorite-amphibole schist or chlorite-olivine-serpentine rock.

vein—a regularly shaped elongate mineral body that runs through another type of rock.

weathered—a rock or mineral that has been decomposed due to exposed conditions near the earth's surface or conditions different from the ones in which it was formed.

xenolith—a rock fragment foreign to the igneous rock in which it is found.

Resources

WESTERN NORTH CAROLINA ROCK AND MINERAL MUSEUMS

Grandfather Mountain North Carolina Mineral Exhibit

The entrance to Grandfather Mountain is located on US Hwy. 221, 2 miles north of Linville and 1 mile south of the Blue Ridge Parkway (milepost 305).

One of the finest collections of North Carolina minerals in existence. The centerpiece of the exhibit is the largest amethyst cluster ever found in North America, collected at the Reel Mine in Lincoln County, North Carolina.

Hours of Operation:
Open daily except Christmas Day and Thanksgiving Day, weather permitting in winter.

Spring	8 am to 6 pm
Summer	8 am to 7 pm
Fall	8 am to 6 pm
Winter	8 am to 5 pm

Ticket sales end one hour before closing.

For more information:
www.grandfather.com/museum/museum.htm

Museum of North Carolina Minerals

Located approximately 5 miles east of Spruce Pine on Hwy. 226, just west of the Blue Ridge Parkway at milepost 331.

The museum was founded in 1955 to display the wide variety of rocks and minerals mined locally in the Spruce Pine mining district. Since then, many more minerals from across the state have been added for a total of more than 300 known varieties. Most of the displays in the museum provide an interesting historical perspective on industrial and commercial uses of rocks and minerals.

Hours of Operation:
Open daily 9 am to 5 pm

For more information:
www.mitchell-county.com/festival/museum.html or
http://sherpaguides.com/north_carolina/mountains/black_mountains/museum_nc_minerals.html

Colburn Earth Science Museum

2 South Pack Square, Asheville
828-254-7162

The museum's collection includes over 4,500 specimens from North Carolina and around the world, along with ores and historical photographs. More than 350 of these are native to North Carolina. Over 1,000 specimens are cut gemstones.

Hours of operation:
Tuesday through Saturday
10 am to 5 pm
Sundays 1 pm to 5 pm

Admission is $4 for adults, $3 for senior citizens and children. Free for children age 4 and under. Group discounts are available as well as discounted passes for admission to other Pack Place members:
Asheville Art Museum
The Health Adventure
YMI Cultural Center

For more information:
www.colburnmuseum.org

Resources (cont'd)

Franklin Gem and Mineral Museum
2 West Main St., Franklin
828-369-7831

The museum, located in the old Macon County jail, has a large collection of rocks and minerals from all over the world and features an abundance of North Carolina varieties. The museum contains a sizable darkroom complete with ultraviolet lights to display an assortment of fluorescent minerals.

Hours of operation:
Open May 1 to October 31

Monday through Saturday
10 am to 4 pm
Sunday 1 pm to 4 pm
Admission is free.

For more information:
www.sherpaguides.com/north_carolina/mountains/nantahala_mountains/macon_gem_mines.html

Ruby City Gems
44 East Main St., Franklin
828-524-3967

The museum reflects over 30 years of collecting specimens and artifacts. The world's largest sapphire, weighing 385 pounds, is on display. A large section under ultraviolet light shows off fluorescent minerals.

Hours of operation:
Open April through December
Monday through Saturday
9 am to 5 pm

Winter Hours:
Tuesday and Thursday
10 am to 3 pm
Admission is free.

For more information:
www.rubycity.com

Mineral & Lapidary Museum of Henderson County, Inc.
400 North Main St., Hendersonville
828-698-1977

The museum displays an impressive collection of rocks, minerals, and cut gems from North Carolina and around the world.

Hours of operation:
Monday through Friday
1 pm to 5 pm
(Open to school groups on weekdays from 9 am to noon, by appointment)
Saturdays 10 am to 5 pm
Admission is free.

For more information:
www.hendersonville.com/news/mining.html
Email: minlap@henderson.main.nc.us

SELECTED ROCK AND MINERAL CLUBS

North Carolina

Asheville—SOUTHERN APPALACHIAN MINERAL SOCIETY INC.
Federations: AFMS, SFMS
PO Box 9306 (28815)
Meetings: 1st Monday, 7 pm
Murphy-Oakley Community Center
749 Fairview Rd.
www.main.nc.us/sams

Chapel Hill—CENTRAL NORTH CAROLINA MINERAL CLUB
1435 Bluff Trail (27514)
Meetings: 1st Tuesday, 7:30 pm
Chapel Hill Senior Center
400 S. Elliott Rd.
Email: ewise1@nc.rr.com

Charlotte—CHARLOTTE GEM & MINERAL CLUB
PO Box 10233 (28212)
Meetings: 3rd Thursday, 7:30 pm
Charlotte Nature Museum
1658 Sterling Rd.
www.charlottegem.freeservers.com

Conover—WESTERN PIEDMONT MINERAL & GEM SOCIETY
PO Box 1098 (28613)
Meetings: 3rd Friday, 7 pm
Conover Municipal Bldg.

Franklin—GEM & MINERAL SOCIETY OF FRANKLIN, NC, INC.
Federations: SFMS, AFMS
25 Phillips St. (28734)
Meetings: Last Thursday, 7:30 pm
Macon County Community Facilities Bldg.
US 441 South
For information call: 828-369-7831
Email: willa@dnet.net

Gastonia—CAPE FEAR MINERAL & GEM SOCIETY
PO Box 953 (28054)
Meetings: 2nd Tuesday, 7 pm
Cliffdale Branch Library
Cliffdale Rd., Fayetteville
John Paschal, President
Email: jpaschal@pinehurst.net

Gastonia—GASTON COUNTY GEM & MINERAL CLUB
c/o Schiele Museum
1500 E. Garrison Blvd. (28053)
Meetings: 4th Thursday, 7 pm
Schiele Museum of Natural History
1500 E. Garrison Blvd.
Contact: Jim Lynn

Greensboro—GREENSBORO GEM & MINERAL CLUB
PO Box 13087 (27415)
Meetings: 1st Monday, 7 pm
New Garden Friends Meeting
801 New Garden Rd.
Joseph McGuire, President
Email: joe_mcguire@prodigy.net

Hayesville—CLAY COUNTY GEM & MINERAL SOCIETY
PO Box 313 (28904)
Meetings: 2nd Tuesday, 1:30 pm
Clay County Senior Center
Contact: B. J. Johnson
Email: eskie@dnet.net.

Resources (continued)

Hendersonville—HENDERSON COUNTY GEM & MINERAL SOCIETY
PO Box 6391 (28793)
Meetings: 3rd Friday, 7:30 pm (except Dec.)
Salvation Army
239 3rd Ave.
Contact: Margaret Johnson

Hickory—CATAWBA VALLEY GEM & MINERAL CLUB, INC.
PO Box 2521 (28603)
Meetings: 2nd Tuesday, 7:30 pm
Holy Trinity Lutheran Church
547 6th St. NW
Contact: Kathleen Bolick

Hickory—CATAWBA VALLEY JUNIOR ROCKHOUNDS
PO Box 2521 (28603)
Meetings: 1st Saturday, 10 am (Feb., May, Aug. & Nov.)
Bolick's
1361 21st Ave. NE

High Point - HIGH POINT GEM & MINERAL CLUB
c/o Arthur Oates
305 Gregg Street (27263)
Meetings: 1st Tuesday, 7 pm
Archdale United Methodist Church
Fellowship Hall
Corner of Hwy. 311 and Petty St.
Archdale
E-mail: oatesla@hpe.infi.net
www.geocities.com/CapeCanaveral/8208

Pittsboro—CHATHAM COUNTY ROCK, GEM, & MINERAL CLUB
Federation: SFMS
PO Box 14 (27312)
Meetings: 2nd Tuesday, 7 pm
Usually Pittsboro Memorial Library in downtown Pittsboro
Email: Douglas Hill: inclusions@mindspring.com or Rich Hayes: rdhayes@mindspring.com

Raleigh—TARHEEL GEM & MINERAL CLUB, INC.
114 Lattimore Lane (27713)
Meetings: 3rd Tuesday, 7:30 pm
Powell Drive Community Center
Robin Suddaby, President
Email: suddaby@mindspring.com

Reidsville —ROCKINGHAM COUNTY MINERAL CLUB
840 Lake LeMar Rd. (27320)
Meetings: 1st Tuesday, 7 pm
Penn Carriage House
324 Maple Ave.
James H. Jones, President
Email: turbo1@surfree.com

Robbinsville—GRAHAM COUNTY MINERALOGICAL SOCIETY
PO Box 1603 (28771)

Rutherford College—NORTH CAROLINA ROCK & MINERAL SOCIETY
PO Box 303 (28671)
Meetings: 2nd Thursday, 7 pm
City Hall

Shelby—ROCKING GEM & MINERAL CLUB
2523 S. Lafayette St. (28152)
Meetings: 1st Tuesday, 7 pm
Chamber of Commerce Bldg.

Winston-Salem—FORSYTH GEM & MINERAL CLUB, INC.
PO Box 21414 (27120)
Meetings: 3rd Thursday, 7:30 pm
Vulcan Materials Company
Lowell Baker, President
Email: baker@ols.net

Georgia

Athens—ATHENS ROCK & GEM CLUB
150 Walton Creek Road (30607)
Meetings: 3rd Thursday
Friendship Christian Church
285 Tallassee Rd.
Jim Maudsley, President
Email: crystals@negia.net
www.mykodi.com/argc

Atlanta - Chamblee—THE GEORGIA MINERAL SOCIETY, INC.
PO Box 15011 (30333)
Meetings: 1st Monday (usually) 7:30 pm
Dunwoody Library
5339 Chamblee-Dunwoody Rd.
Joan White Waggener, President
Email: president@gamineral.org

Augusta—AUGUSTA GEM & MINERAL SOCIETY
2102 Cook Rd. (30904)
Meetings: 3rd Friday, 8 pm
Daniel Village Branch of First Union Bank
(off Iris Street and Central Ave.)
Wrightsboro Rd.
Ray Ireland, President
or Glen Williams at 803-737-5531
www.AugustaGMS.Homestead.com/AGMS1.html

Cornelia—NORTHEAST GEORGIA MINERAL SOCIETY
PO Box 185 (30531-0185)
Meetings: 1st Thursday, 7:30 pm
Cornelia Library
Pat Steinmetz, President
Email: E.T.Dibble at edible@rabun.net
www.america.net/~butch

Carrollton—CARROLL COUNTY GEM & MINERAL SOCIETY
Federations: SFMS, AFMS
105 Plantation Ave. (30117)
Meetings: 2nd Thursday, 7:30
Neva Lomasson Library
Rome St.
Jorie Billingsly, President
http://ccgms.us

Gainesville—LANIER GEM & MINERAL SOCIETY, INC.
3527 Casper Dr., #65-C (30506)
3rd Tuesday, 7:30 pm
Blackshear Public Library
2927 Atlanta Hwy.
Richard Walter, President

Marietta—COBB COUNTY GEM & MINERAL SOCIETY
PO Box 680812 (30068)
Meetings: 2nd Tuesday, 7:30 pm
East Cobb Gov't. Center
4400 Lower Roswell Rd.
Kim Cochran, President

Rome—GEORGIA MINERAL SOCIETY
2505 Old Ced Rd.
Lindale (30147)
Meetings: 2nd Monday, 7:30 pm
Rome-Floyd County Library
Riverside Parkway
Lynn Batts, President

Resources (continued)

Stockbridge—COTTON INDIAN
GEM & MINERAL SOCIETY, INC.
PO Box 472 (30281)
Meetings: 1st Thursday, 7:30 pm
Bethel Methodist Church Parish Hall
Harry Hyaduck, President
E-mail: jackwthompson@bigfoot.com
www.go.to/cottonindianmineral

Young Harris—APPALACHIAN
GEM & MINERAL SOCIETY
PO Box 980 (30582)
Meetings: Varies
William Holland School of Lapidary Art
Suzanne Wagner, Secretary
Email: Lapidary@alltel.net

Tennessee

Knoxville—KNOXVILLE
GEM & MINERAL SOCIETY
725 E. Meadcrest Dr. (37921)
Meetings: 3rd Thursday, 7:30 pm
University of Tennessee
Agricultural Complex
Brehm Animal Sciences Bldg. 1st Floor
Email: dmillerspe@aol.com
www.korrnet.org/kgms

South Carolina

Aiken—AIKEN
GEM & MINERAL SOCIETY
Federations: AGMS, SFMS, EFMLS
3424 Meadow Dr. (29801-2851)
Meetings: Last Friday of January through
October, 8 pm
Room 200 USCA Science Bldg.
University of South Carolina at Aiken
Email Kathleen Wallis at:
wkkw@groupz.net
www.homestead.com/aikengms

Spartanburg—PACOLET
GEM & MINERAL SOCIETY
PO Box 674 (29304)
Meetings: 2nd & 4th Tuesdays, 7:30 pm
T. W. Edwards Recreation Center
Pacolet

Virginia

Lynchburg—GEM & MINERAL SOCIETY
OF LYNCHBURG
PO Box 2348 (24501)
Meetings: 3rd Wednesday, 7 pm
Park & Recreation Bldg. Auditorium
301 Grove St.

Richmond—RICHMOND
GEM & MINERAL SOCIETY
Federation: EFMS
PO Box 26985 (23261)
Meetings: 2nd Wednesday, 7:30 pm
Jewish Community Center of Richmond
5403 Monument Ave.
Contact Persons:
Ruddy Bland, Lyell Warren,
Earl Guertin

NORTH CAROLINA GEM MINES

Alexander County
Emerald Hollow Mine—Hiddenite
828-632-3394

Cabarrus County
Alexander Reed Gold Mine—Georgeville
704-721-4653

Haywood County
Old Pressley Sapphire Mine—Canton
828-648-6320

Macon County
Cherokee Ruby Mine, Franklin
828-524-5684

Cowee Mountain Ruby Mine, Franklin
828-369-5271

Gold City Mine, Franklin
828-369-3905

Jackson Hole Mine, Franklin
828-524-5850

Mason Mtn. Rhodolite Mine, Franklin
828-524-4570

Mason's Sapphire Mine, Franklin
828-369-9742

Moonstone Gem Mine, Franklin
828-524-7764

Rocky Face Mine, Franklin
828-524-3148

Rose Creek Mine, Franklin
828-524-3225

Sheffield Ruby Mine, Franklin
828-369-8383

The Old Cardinal Mine, Franklin
828-369-7534

Mitchell County
Blue Ridge Mine, Little Switzerland
828-765-5264

Emerald Village
828-765-6463

Gem Mountain
828-765-6130

Rio Doce Mine
828-765-2099l

Spruce Pine Gem and Gold Mine
828-765-7981

Stanley County
Cotton Patch Gold Mine, New London
704-463-5797

Watauga County
Foscoe Gem Mining Company, Foscoe
828-963-5928

Magic Mountain Mine, Boone
828-265-4653

References

Asheville (N.C.) Citizen-Times. Roy R. Beck, "Old Haywood Mine Contains Silver, Lead, Copper and Zinc" Section D, June 9, 1957.

Arrangements.com, internet web page www.arrangements.com/history/bmound/bmound.htm.

Beyer, Fred. 1991. *North Carolina, The Years before Man: A Geologic History,* Carolina Academic Press.

Broadhurst, Sam D. 1955. *The Mining Industry in North Carolina from 1946 through 1953*: North Carolina Division of Mineral Resources.

Clayton, Lawrence A., Vernon James Knight, Jr., and Edward Moore (Editors). 1993. *The De Soto Chronicles, the Expedition of Hernando De Soto to North America in 1539-1543*, Volumes I and II, University of Alabama Press.

Conrad, Stephen G. 1960. *Crystalline Limestones of the Piedmont and Mountain Regions of North Carolina*, North Carolina Department of Conservation and Development, Division of Mineral Resources, Bulletin Number 74.

Franklin Area Chamber of Commerce. 2001. *Franklin Area Gem Mines*, internet web address: www.franklin-chamber.com/mine.htm.

Hadley, Jarvis B. 1949. *A Preliminary Report on Corundum Deposits in the Buck Creek Peridotite, Clay County, North Carolina* (pp. 103-128), Strategic Minerals Investigation, United States Department of the Interior, Geological Survey.

Hunter, C. E. 1949. *Report on Barite in the Vicinity of Stackhouse, Madison County, North Carolina*, Regional Minerals Section, Division of Chemical Engineering, Tennessee Valley Authority.

Hunter, C. E., and P. W. Mattocks, 1935. *Feldspar Report on the Deposits in the Vicinity of Democrat, Buncombe County, North Carolina*: Tennessee Valley Authority, open-file report, Knoxville, Tennessee.

Lesure, Frank, et. al. 1968. Mica Deposits of the Blue Ridge in North Carolina: U.S. Geological Survey Professional Paper 577.

Margolin, Peter, R. 1999. Mica Mining at North Carolina's Sink Hole, from Prehistoric Times to the Sputnik Era, *Matrix: A Journal of the History of Minerals*, Volume 7.

Merschat, Carl E. 1993. *Geologic Map and Mineral Resources Summary of the Barnardsville Quadrangle*, North Carolina Department of Natural Resources and Community Development, Division of Land Resources, Geological Survey Section.

Ohiokids.org, internet web address: www.ohiokids.org/fkbk/westerville/pages/hopewell/big%20project/exotic_materials.htm

Olson, Jerry C. 1952. *Pegmatites of the Cashiers and Zirconia Districts, North Carolina*, North Carolina Department of Conservation and Development, Division of Minerals Resources, Bulletin No. 64.

Pratt, Joseph Hyde and Joseph Volney Lewis. 1905. *Corundum and Peridotite of Western North Carolina*, Volume I, North Carolina Geological Survey.

Rankin, H.S. July 11, 1940. *Field Trip June 11, 1940,* by H.S. Rankin and Hunter, Memorandum, Tennessee Valley Authority.

Stuckey, Jasper Leonidas. 1965. *North Carolina: Its Geology and Mineral Resources*, North Carolina Department of Conservation and Development.

United States Department of the Interior. 1943. The Yancey County Kyanite Property, Burnsville, North Carolina, *War Minerals Report*, Regional File No. E-176, Bureau of Mines, College Park, Maryland.

Watts, A. S. 1913. *Mining and Treatment of Feldspar and Kaolin in the Southern Appalachian Region*: U.S. Bureau of Mines Bulletin 53.

Wiener, Leonard S., and Sigrid Ballew. 1995. *A Listing of North Carolina Minerals*, North Carolina Geological Survey, Geologic Note No. 4, Division of Land Resources.

Wiener, Leonard S., and Carl E. Merschat. 1990. *Field Guidebook To the Geology of the Central Blue Ridge of North Carolina and the Spruce Pine Mining District*, North Carolina Geological Survey, Division of Land Resources.

Index (of Minerals and Collecting Sites)

A

Abernathy Mine 78
actinolite 32
albite 90, 104
almandine garnet 42, 66
amazonite 104
apatite 78, 82, 104
aquamarine 86, 104
aragonite 94
autunite 84
azurite 54

B

Bandana Dolomite Marble 80
banded marble 94
barite 70
Behr Corundum Mine 40
beryl 60, 86, 104
Black Mountain Kyanite 26
Buck Creek 42

C

calcite 22, 74, 94
cerussite 54
chalcedony 28
Chalk Mountain Mine 84
Chambers Mountain Kyanite 48
chlorite schist 66
chromite 28
chrysocolla 54
columbite 104
corundum 26, 40, 42, 44, 50, 52, 98
Corundum Knob 44
Crabtree Emerald Mine 86
Cranberry Iron Mine 22

D

Deer Park Mine 88
dog tooth calcite 74
dravite 32

E

edenite 44
emerald 86
epidote 22

F

feldspar 44, 60, 78, 82, 84, 86, 88, 104
fluorite 70, 104

G

galena 54
garnet 22, 28, 42, 58, 66, 78, 80, 82, 86, 88, 90, 102
golden beryl 86, 104
Goldsmith Mine 28
Grimshawe Mine 98

H

hedenbergite 22
hematite 40
Hitchcock Mine 32
Hootowl Mine 90
hyalite 84, 88

K

kyanite 26, 48, 80, 82, 102

L

limonite 34
Little Pine Garnet Mine 66

M

magnetite 22
malachite 54
marble 32, 80, 94
Mas-Celo Kyanite Mine 102
mica 60

mica schist 58
microcline 104
monazite 88
moonstone 28
Murphy Limonite after Pyrite 34
muscovite 78, 82, 88, 90, 104

N

Nantahala Talc & Limestone Quarry 94

O

Old Pressley Sapphire Mine 52
oligoclase 104
olivine 28, 44
opal 84
orthoclase 22, 90

P

pink orthoclase 22
plagioclase feldspar 104
pyrite 34, 54, 94
pyromorphite 54

Q

quartz 60, 74, 86, 88, 90, 94
quartz with phantoms 74

R

Ray (Wray) Mine 104
Redmond Prospect 54
ruby 40, 44, 98
Ruby City 58

S

sapphire 40, 44, 50, 52, 98
schorl 104
serpentine 28, 42
serpentine minerals 44
Sheepcliff Mine 60
Shut-In Creek Unakite 68
Sinkhole Mine 82
smoky quartz 86, 88, 90
speleothems 94
sphalerite 54
Stackhouse Mines 70
staurolite 36

T

talc 32, 94
thulite 88
torbernite 84
tourmaline 32, 86
travertine 94
tremolite 32, 94

U

unakite 68

V

Vengeance Creek 36
vermiculite 28

W

white feldspar 28
white microcline 104
wollastonite 80
Wood Creek 50
Woodlawn Limestone Quarry 74
Wray Mine 104

Z

zoisite 44

Field Notes

Milestone Press

Outdoor Adventure Guides

OFF THE BEATEN TRACK
MOUNTAIN BIKE GUIDE SERIES
by Jim Parham

- Vol. I: Western NC–Smokies
- Vol. II: Western NC–Pisgah
- Vol. III: North Georgia
- Vol. IV: East Tennessee
- Vol. V: Northern Virginia

ROAD BIKE SERIES

- Road Bike Asheville, NC:
  Favorite Rides of the Blue Ridge Bicycle Club
  by The Blue Ridge Bicycle Club

- Road Bike the Smokies:
  16 Great Rides in North Carolina's Great Smoky Mountains
  by Jim Parham

- Road Bike North Georgia:
  25 Great Rides in the Mountains and Valleys of North Georgia
  by Jim Parham

Can't find the Milestone Press book you want at a bookseller near you?
Don't despair—you can order it directly from us.
Call us at 828-488-6601
or shop on line at
www.milestonepress.com.

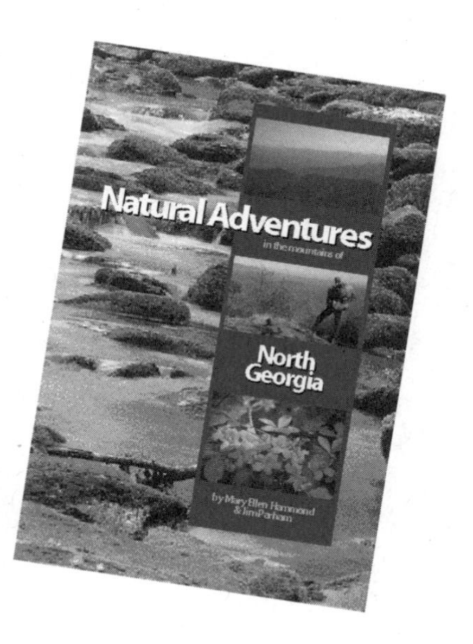

PLAYBOATING

• Playboating the Nantahala River
  An Entry Level Guide
  by Kelly Fischer

FAMILY ADVENTURES

• Natural Adventures in the Mountains
  of North Georgia
  by Mary Ellen Hammond
  & Jim Parham

Milestone Press
Outdoor Adventure Guides

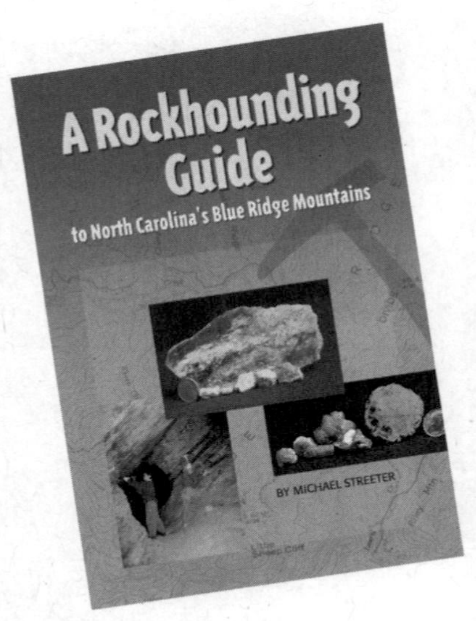

ROCKHOUNDING

- A Rockhounding Guide to North Carolina's Blue Ridge Mountains by Michael Streeter

MOTORCYCLE ADVENTURE SERIES
by Hawk Hagebak

- Motorcycle Adventures in the Southern Appalachians– North GA, East TN, Western NC (Book 1)
- Motorcycle Adventures in the Southern Appalachians– Asheville NC, Blue Ridge Parkway, NC High Country (Book 2)
- Motorcycle Adventures in the Central Appalachians– Virginia's Blue Ridge, Shenandoah Valley, West Virginia Highlands (Book 3)

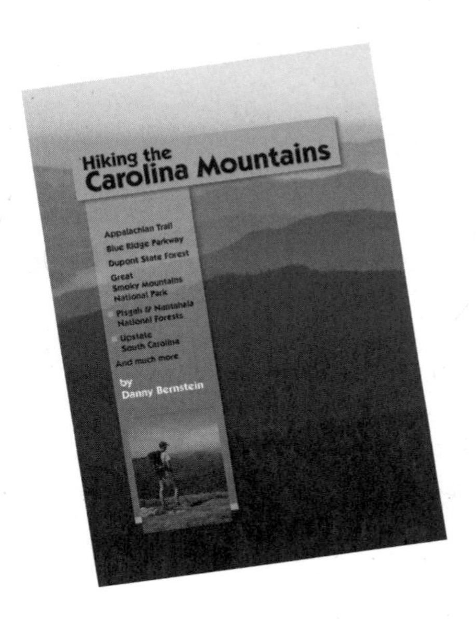

HIKING GUIDES

- Hiking the Carolina Mountains
  by Danny Bernstein

- Hiking North Carolina's
  Blue Ridge Heritage
  by Danny Bernstein

- Waterfall Hikes of North Georgia
  by Jim Parham

- Waterfall Hikes of
  Upstate South Carolina
  by Thomas E. King

Can't find the Milestone Press book you want at a bookseller near you?
Don't despair—you can order it directly from us.
Call us at 828-488-6601
or shop on line at
www.milestonepress.com.

Ruby in edenite-amphibolite (p. 44)

White dolomitic marble (p. 80)

Apatite in pegmatite (p. 78)

Apatite in mica (p. 78)

Ruby and sapphire (p. 40)

Hyalite opal (p. 84)

Torbernite on quartz (p. 84)

Corundum in matrix and pieces (p. 42)

Wollastonite on marble (p. 80)

Almadine garnet (p. 42)

Kyanite (p. 26)

Kyanite in matrix (p. 48)

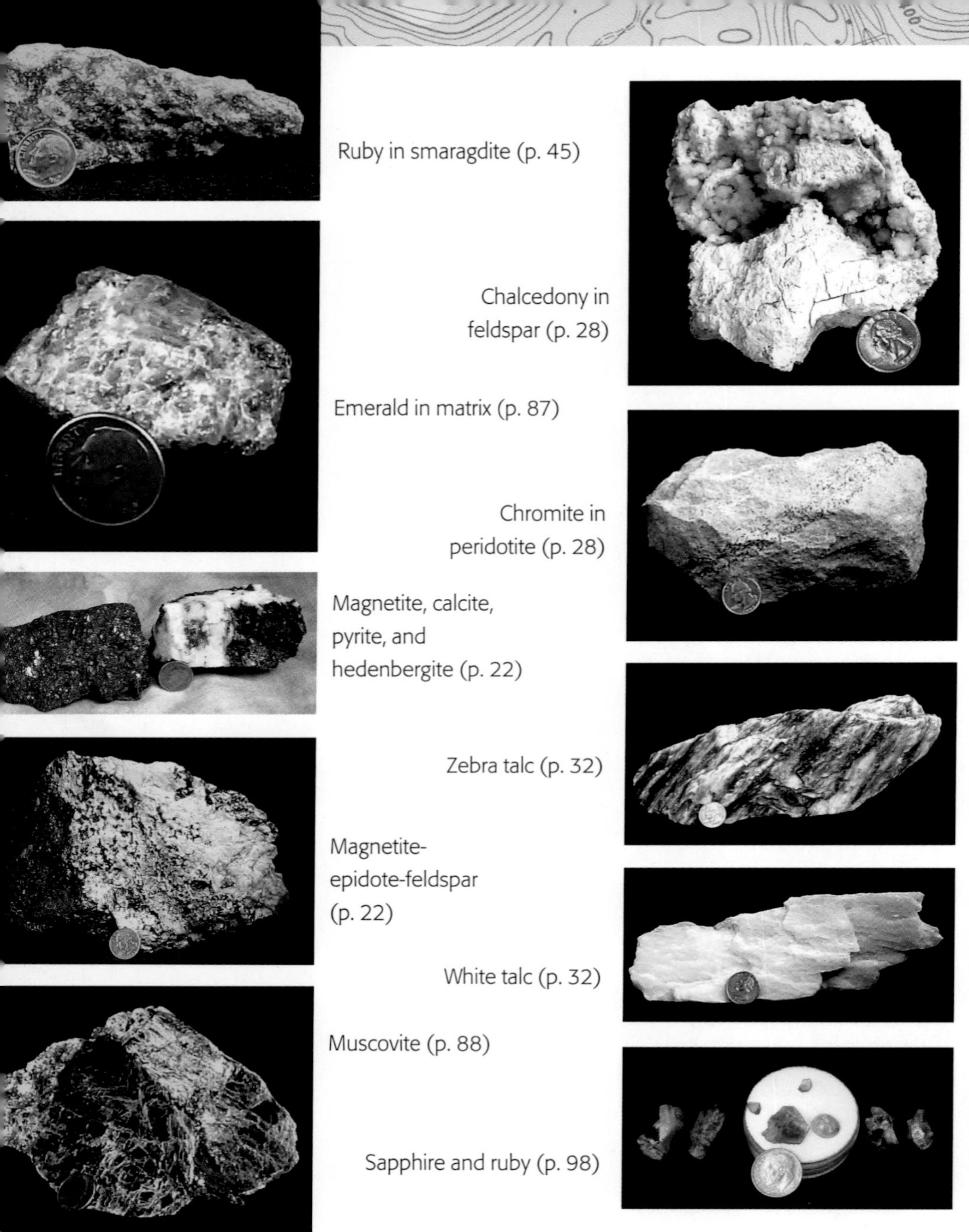

Ruby in smaragdite (p. 45)

Chalcedony in feldspar (p. 28)

Emerald in matrix (p. 87)

Chromite in peridotite (p. 28)

Magnetite, calcite, pyrite, and hedenbergite (p. 22)

Zebra talc (p. 32)

Magnetite-epidote-feldspar (p. 22)

White talc (p. 32)

Muscovite (p. 88)

Sapphire and ruby (p. 98)

Garnet in mica (p. 88)

Banded marble (p. 94)

Travertine dripstone (p. 94)

Muscovite, feldspar, and quartz pegmatite (p. 90)

Limonite after pyrite (p. 34)

Almandine garnet crystals (p. 66)

Kyanite (p. 103)

Garnet in schist (p. 66)

Amazonite, fluorite, and feldspar (p. 104)

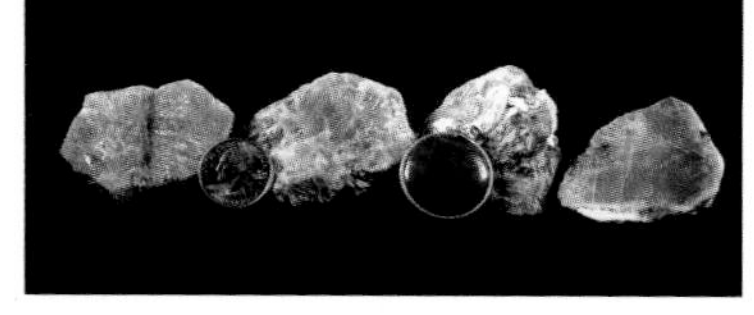

Sapphire crystals (p. 52)

Aquamarine crystals (p. 104)

Sapphire crystal (p. 52)

Cerussite and chrysocolla on limonite and quartz (p. 55)

Barite (p. 70)

Rhodolite garnet in schist (p. 58)

Staurolite crystals (p. 36)

Beryl crystals and pieces (p. 61)

Quartz plate (p. 74)

Unakite (p. 68)

Sapphire (p. 50)

Apatite in pegmatite (p. 82)

Sapphire (p. 50)

Feldspar (p. 82)